Michael Sleggs is probably
Slugs on the BBC BAFTA
Country. However, those w............... ...., ... a
born entertainer who was always able to see the funny side of
things despite the many difficulties that life threw his way.

Michael had numerous complex heart operations for his
congenital heart defects. During these he also suffered two
strokes. He subsequently spent a further six months at Great
Ormond Street Hospital as an inpatient when he was
diagnosed with a non-Hodgkins lymphoma during his
GCSEs. Despite his poor health, Michael still lived a full and
happy life – he went to amazing places, had fantastic friends
and enjoyed a range of interesting jobs culminating in the
ultimate honour – acting alongside friends in a hit TV
comedy! A life complete, he courageously bowed out on 9th
July 2019, aged 33 – the same age as his ultimate hero.

This book was in the final stages of publication just as
Michael died. Michael had become concerned that some of
what he had written might unintentionally offend or hurt
individuals. He realised that he wouldn't be around to defend
his book or to reassure those mentioned within that he cared
for them more than the book might suggest. Therefore, one of
his dying wishes was that we, as his family, would read
through the book and remove or change anything we felt
might cause offense. This has inevitably led to a delay in the
publication, but we hope that you will feel it was worth it. We
are now keen to publish this book in his memory – so that
others can appreciate, as much as we have, his talent for
entertaining and telling a tall tale. We miss him every day, and
we are heartened that we are not alone in this. He touched the
lives of so many people in his relatively short life and we hope
that he can continue to do so with this book.

For Daisy.

Michael Sleggs

MEMOIRS OF A '90S SCHOOLBOY

AUSTIN MACAULEY PUBLISHERS™

LONDON • CAMBRIDGE • NEW YORK • SHARJAH

Author's Note: I have tried to recreate events, locales and conversations from my memories of them. In order to maintain their anonymity in some instances, I have changed the names of individuals and places; I may have changed some identifying characteristics and details such as physical properties, occupations and places of residence.

A CIP catalogue record for this title is available from the British Library.

ISBN 9781528934077 (Paperback)
ISBN 9781528967723 (ePub e-book)

www.austinmacauley.com

First Published (2020)
Austin Macauley Publishers Ltd
25 Canada Square
Canary Wharf
London
E14 5LQ

First and foremost I would like to thank Daisy Cooper for inspiring me to write this book. I would also like to thank my sister, Tara Beedle, for something (not sure what) and Lucy Wilkins for proofreading the first draft. To all the people I went to primary school with and all the stories you have provided me with (even if they were just in my imagination) — thank you, this book would not be possible without you!

Introduction

This book first began as a simple text to a friend who enquired about someone we both knew. She has always had a fascination with certain people, usually oddballs. This was not attraction, but just fascination, about them, their lives, their actions, what makes them tick. The person in question was a lad I went to school with named Kevin Blankenhorn (now Richards). So I sent her a quick text recalling some of my memories of childhood and going around his house for dinner. He had always been a pebble in my shoe, and I was not shy to express that. She thought it was so hysterical she told me to write more. This went on for several months till I eventually conceded to writing her a book on the matter. The book in question is this one. However, as the book progressed, it has not only become a book solely about Kevin but about a lot of people I grew up with: friends and foe. The majority of it is set at my primary school where I spent my early years and so acquired an extensive catalogue of memories and anecdotes which are shared within these pages. The stories are, however, meant to be taken with a pinch of salt, as they are either true, partially true or completely made up for the comedy. The names of some of the characters have been changed to spare their embarrassment. The stories within were seen through the lens of a child and therefore some exaggeration can be expected. I am also featured as not entirely my true self: more a caricature of the way I was (although, saying that, most of my self-representations are pretty accurate). The book begins at Kevin's birth, clearly an event I was neither present at nor privy to (nor would I have wanted to be) but, from my uneducated, unprofessional and nonsensical position, I have confidently deduced how things went down that night. Oh, and one last thing, since it's an obscure term, I should probably use this opportunity to explain the word 'chungs' means double chin/wattle. Yeah, I think that's all I need to put here. Enjoy the read...

Chapter 1

Home Birthing

It was a dark and stormy night. Outside the wind howled as the rain pitter-pattered on the living room window. The faint sound of the gate crashing and knocking against its post could be heard from afar.

"Push. PUSH!" barked Mr Blankenhorn in his wife's ear as she lay spread eagle, naked, on the couch in front of him.

"Push!!!" he yelled again, this time sounding less encouraging and more impatient as if he was running late for pressing engagement elsewhere.

"I'm pushing as hard as I can, love. It's just bloody roasting in 'ere," Mrs Blankenhorn retorted.

"I'll get you a cold cloth," Mr Blankenhorn replied as he darted out of the room toward the kitchen.

In the kitchen, two children, a boy and a girl, sat waiting very patiently. In a lapse of judgement and excitement, the boy hopped to his feet when he saw his father enter the room.

"Is it here yet, Daddy, is it here yet!?" squealed the young boy.

Mr Blankenhorn, fixated on his mission, brashly replied, "Not yet, Tom!" Mr Blankenhorn kicked the boy aside, sending him careering into the cheap plywood cabinet beneath the sink, knocking him off his feet and the cabinet off its hinges in the process. Meanwhile, the little girl stood by, not making a sound save nervously finger popping her cheek repeatedly.

"Now where was I?" muttered a flustered Mr Blankenhorn to himself. "Ah, yes." He violently grabbed a handful of kitchen roll with his banana-like fingers, about five-and-a-half slices torn messily in the middle, choosing not to utilise the premade perforation at the end of each slice. Next, he slammed on the cold tap in the kitchen sink which began to fill. This task was made quicker by the displacement of space caused by a multitude of dirty dishes that had been left to fester for the past three months sitting idly in the basin. Instead of removing the dishes, he simply dunked the five-and-a-half slices of kitchen roll in the dirty dishwater in the in-between space between the rancid crockery. The kitchen roll was immediately saturated. This was in days long before 'thirst pockets', the Rolls Royce of kitchen rolls we take for granted today that can actually absorb a substantial load without leaking or tearing. In mere seconds, Mr Blankenhorn retrieved his mushy wad of sopping tissue from the filthy sink and stormed out of the kitchen back towards the living room, pausing only to grab a carrot out of a plastic bag that was hanging from the doorknob on the way out. Meanwhile, Tom was still lying dazed in the kitchen corner against the cabinet but, admirably, had not made a peep since the incident.

Back in the living room, Mrs Blankenhorn had turned beetroot red and was screaming at the top of her lungs. A long bulging, blue vein had begun to appear and snake its way down from the top of her head to the bottom of her neck. Every time she clenched, the vein throbbed and pulsated. The couch was soaked in sweat and had turned from grey to patchy darker grey. The air was thick with the smell of ripe BO, greasy hair and animal feed. Condensation misted the glass clock face above the TV and the window at the end of the couch.

Mr Blankenhorn stood awkwardly by checking his watch. "Here, honey, this'll help!" he snorted, as he clumsily threw the drenched wad of tissue towards her forehead. It splatted like a cow pat across her face, the majority of it, in fairness hitting her forehead, but the remainder speckling her face, glasses and lips like the aggressive wake of a cluster bomb detonation.

"Thanks, babes," she replied as she licked the tissue residue from her lips. Mr Blankenhorn moved his head in closer towards his wife's.

"Bite down on this, it'll help," ordered Mr Blankenhorn as he forcefully thrust the carrot he had hastily grabbed from the kitchen into her mouth.

"That's the pig's dinner! It's not fair on her!" Mrs Blankenhorn mumbled as best as she could around the carrot.

"Never mind that!" shouted Mr Blankenhorn, visibly cross at this stage. "Just bite down hard and squeeze." He wiped sweat from his own brow.

There was one final quiet whimper, like an old stinky golden retriever feeling the point of the euthanasia needle at the vet's, as the climax of birth pain tugged at Mrs Blankenhorn' vulva. As this happened, a bulbous head peered from her vagina followed quickly by a husky, stout, but small little body. It was ten past nine in the evening on the 23rd of August, 1985 when Kevin Blankenhorn finally slithered out of his mother and into our world. She was exhausted. The end half of the couch cushion was now fully waterlogged and sodden with blood, sweat and afterbirth. Despite the smell, which by this point was mounting on skunk-like proportions (and could be proven by the fact that a canary had dropped dead in its cage in the corner of the room during the ordeal), Mr Blankenhorn stood proud. That was until he reached down to pick young Kevin up.

"My boy!" he said haughtily, although there was a hint of inquisitiveness to it, as if to slyly illicit some kind of confession out of Mrs Blankenhorn. An awkward silence descended upon the room. At this point, Mr Blankenhorn who had been staring sceptically at the baby's jellyfish face for a long moment lifted him up above his head with pride coming to the conclusion that all was well.

"Well, he's a Blankenhorn, alright!" he stated. No sooner had he proclaimed so when Kevin's head caught the end of the rusty, spinning fan blade that was hanging from the ceiling knocking him out of his father's butterfingers clear across the room.

"Whoops," chuckled Mr Blankenhorn sheepishly as he headed towards Kevin who had luckily broken his fall by landing on and crushing one of the many pet rabbits that were scuttling about the floor.

"You daft sod, give 'im 'ere. I wanna cuddle," Mrs Blankenhorn joked as she got up, flipped the couch cushion over to the clean side and sat back down, all the while still stark-billy-bollock naked. Mr Blankenhorn handed Kevin over to his mother, lit a cigarette, and shouted out of the corner of his mouth:

"Kids, you can come through now. You've got a new baby brother."

A moment later, the two children came screaming and giggling into the room and sat next to their mother cawing and cooing at the baby. At the same time, a vast tongue emerged from Mrs Blankenhorn' mouth, and she began to lick Kevin's head and body, much like a mother cat bathing her kittens. Mrs Blankenhorn had an oddly massive tongue, like a cow's tongue. It was a wonder it all fit in her mouth. It was difficult at this point to tell if the tongue was a hereditary issue or just a random isolated genetic anomaly, but the Blankenhorn tongue could explain why Kevin felt the need to shout everything he said at school in later years (as if to compensate for the bad diction he may have had due to a grossly enlarged tongue). But we'll cross that bridge when we get to it.

By now, the two children who were sitting next to their mother had started to yawn, but just as young Tom's eyes began to close, he remembered something. He, suddenly, jumped up and very proudly announced, "Me and Angela have a surprise. We made Kevin a crib to sleep in!"

Tom rushed into the kitchen and grabbed their crib and came back as quick as a flash! "Here it is!" he said, presenting what was really just a cardboard box decorated with poorly-coloured, pre-drawn pictures stuck on the sides sloppily with an embarrassing overabundance of Sellotape. Tom beamed with delight as he thought he and his sister had been very diligent in keeping within the lines in the colouring process. Tom was wrong. The colouring looked terrible! Spastic.

"Oh, that's very sweet. Thanks, darlings!" Mrs Blankenhorn said softly, her tongue now back in her massive, over-stretched gob.

No sooner had this pleasant moment occurred when it was rudely replaced by petty squabbling as Angela snatched the box out of Tom's hands, crying, "I want to give it to him!"

"NO! It was mostly my project. I'm giving it to him!" Tom exploded.

The two kids crashed to the floor wrestling each other. Angela stretched her hand out and opened the hamster pen a foot away from her. She moved expertly despite being punched, kicked and clung to by a ruffled-feathered Tom. Eventually, young Angela's clawing fist reached the distressed hamster who was cowering in the corner of the cage, pulled it out and yanked at Tom's trousers stuffing the very active hamster inside. Tom jumped back and jiggled, his eyes wide with rage and worry. Finally, he kicked the hamster out of the bottom of his left leg on his trousers. A hamster piss stain ran thinly down the length of Tom's trouser leg as it had uncontrollably evacuated its bladder in fear on the journey down. It seemed like milliseconds, but it was enough time for Angela to hand the box/crib to her mum and pat baby Kevin uselessly as she put him inside.

It was getting late now, around 10 pm, and the darkness of night had arrived. Tom and Angela crawled off to bed leaving Mr and Mrs Blankenhorn in the living room with baby Kevin who was fast asleep, snoring and snorting like a wild boar in his box by the fireplace. It had been a very exciting day in the Blankenhorn house as the whole circle of life pantomime had played out among their four walls. The tally for the day: one new life (Kevin); and two deaths (the canary and the squashed rabbit). Unlike most houses, this was a very respectable score for the Blankenhorn household as pet deaths ran rampant in their home. The canary and rabbit were merely statistics at this stage; they would not be missed sorely.

"Well. This calls for a little celebration, don't you think?" Mr Blankenhorn said winking at his husk of a wife who was curled next to him. She was only now discovering little bits of tissue about her face and gently pawing them off.

"We've got nothing in the house!" she yawned.

"No matter, my dearest. I'll pop down to Threshers and pick us up a bottle of Lambrini. I think they're open till eleven," he replied nonchalantly, picking up his keys.

"Don't be gone long, my darling," Mrs Blankenhorn whispered as Mr Blankenhorn left the house, quietly closing the door behind him. She heard the faint roar of his Lada engine whistle through the curtains as she closed her eyes. A dim shadow whisked across the room as the car drove past.

Mr Blankenhorn never returned home.

Chapter 2
First Day of St Paul's

Five long years had passed since the fateful events of that night in August of 1985, and Kevin, the spawn of that dreadful evening, had been growing like a cancerous tumour.

The year was 1990. It was a blustery September morning the first time I stepped onto the playground of St Paul's in my mint-condish uniform. I had bidden farewell to my mum, and with my rucksack slung tightly upon my shoulders, my Mickey Mouse head shaped lunchbox gripped firmly in my left hand and my book bag, (which in the early 90s was merely an oversized rectangle see through plastic ziplock baggie, with a colour zip, mine was yellow) in my right, I entered reception, aka Class One. Upon arrival, I sat down on the floor whilst two old ladies, Mrs Rose and Miss Lily, called our names and pointed us into one of two designated groups, much like two guards on the Burma Death Railway in the Second World War splitting lines between prisoners to die and prisoners fit to work. Fortunately, despite the odd asthma attack by Rachel Farmer who had forgotten her inhaler that day, no one was going to die. Unfortunately, we were all going to have to work.

Once the lines had been drawn between the classes, my class was separated into the next room. I looked around at my peers to see who had survived the Class Two cull. For the most part, the segregation, I felt, had done us good: it kept most of my preferred acquaintances and friends from Lewis Lane Playgroup together whilst separating the chaff of unknown weirdoes and dumbasses like Darren Bisset and Ben Fields into the other class for the other teacher to deal with. However, like too many things in life left to the chance of human error, it wasn't a clean break. Whilst the severance had been fairly successful, sadly (like a water filter damaged in transit to some third world country) it failed to sift all of the human waste from the group. As I panned my eyes around my class registering and okaying the fruit of Miss Lily's labour, my smile suddenly dropped. There, fiddling with his apparent 'stuck drawer', was Kevin Blankenhorn. Of course, at this point, I didn't know him, but I was quickly able to make some very astute and accurate assumptions simply by observing him. For one, it was the first day of school, and this boy had already managed to spill strawberry yoghurt and toothpaste down his new school uniform. This must have been done at home because break time wasn't for another hour. The cuffs on his jumper were tatty and had bite marks fraying at the end of them. His undershirt, grey polyester, had managed to untuck itself at the back and was hanging out over his massive bottom, whilst the front half was tightly and messily shoved into the front side of his trousers, some of it even coming through his flies, which were broken and hanging loose. His trouser button was hanging on for dear life, whilst the button threading was beginning to unravel every time he breathed. His hair was messy and unkempt; it looked to be thick yet thinning at the same time, hay-like: a real-life optical illusion. Wherever this kid had come from, it was clear he had been dragged through the back of a bush on his journey here. Or maybe a few bushes.

Pushing prejudices and judgments aside for a minute, I thought to myself: *No, Michael. You must give this lad a chance. Who knows? He could be really cool.* So admirably, despite the one look of disgust by my fellow classmates, I approached this young boy.

"Hi, I'm Michael. What's your name?" I said, nicely, extending an olive branch to the new token class pariah.

"KEVIN," he bellowed loudly back, grinning from pig's ear to pig's ear.

For a moment, everything went quiet. I felt like Tom Hanks in *Saving Private Ryan* when the beach mine detonates near him in Normandy, and he temporarily loses his hearing. Fear washed over me, much like Tom Hanks in Saving Private Ryan during the same scene I mentioned in the previous simile. I staggered around the classroom dazed, feeling my way round the desks and chairs for support, whilst looking up and seeing my class mates mouth the words, "What's wrong?" and "Michael, can you hear me?" Silence turned to whistling. Then sound rushed back to my ear canals as they re-orientated themselves back to normality. Furious and with a pounding headache, I sat down far away from Kevin.

We began the class by watching Words and Pictures, followed by Finger mouse. Aside from the off-putting sound of occasional farting, followed by juvenile tittering and a pant wetting by the one kid who always wet himself (in this case, Richard Slate), the morning went off without a hitch. It was soon snack time, and we all formed an orderly queue to collect our milk and head outside for play. Fortunately, I was well ahead of Kevin in the queue. Kevin had fallen behind and was busy scratching his knee (probably due to an unchecked rash that had been left to linger and spread unabated). *Gross,* I thought to myself and headed out the door.

Outside, the sun had begun to shine, and I soon located my best friend, Sam Barnsley. Sam Barnsley was a cool dude, easy to get on with, had similar interests (Teenage Mutant Ninja Turtles) and was genuinely just a nice guy. Next, we hooked up with Steve McDougal, a strong up-and-comer and candidate for best friend spot, despite being born and raised on the wrong side of the tracks, or in this case, a chavvy council estate in Bowling Green Avenue. Steve was testament to the phrase, you can't judge a book by its cover. Truth is, I had known both boys since Lewis Lane Playgroup and, this being first day of school, it felt good to break myself in gently with some familiar faces and as a bonus be rid of that wretched Kevin character. We played a round of hopscotch. Then we were waved over by Alex Carter, a kid who had the most circular shaped head I had seen in my whole life. At least, that was until I reached Secondary School and laid my eyes upon Patrick O'Malley, a boy with a head so perfectly spherical, there was a rumour FIFA had offered him a substantial cheque for a cast of his head to mould their new line of 'perfect sphere' footballs.

"Wanna play stuck in the mud?" Alex asked.

"Yeah!"

"Sounds good!"

"Yep!"

"Sure!" It was unanimous. We each placed our right foot towards each other making a perfect mathematical times symbol between the four of us in the middle. Alex, who had arranged the game, began to point at each foot singing the selection song, as was customary:

"Ip, dip, dog shit you are not…" Alex began, but just as he was about to eliminate me from the drudgery and more athletic work of being 'it', the song was rudely interrupted.

"Want some water, Mike!?" boomed a foul voice from the far end of the playground. It was the same foul voice that had blasted my eardrums at the beginning of class that morning and would have done so again if it wasn't for the grace of a healthy safe distance. As I raised my head, already annoyed that I had mostly likely lost my best chance at evading being 'it', I spotted Kevin's fat, heavy face poised over the water fountain staring at me, his eyes glazed with a stupid vacant look. For a moment, he looked like Hooch from Turner and Hooch after he had just savaged a bowl of water during an unquenchable thirst rage. His dumb, cow-like face was dappled with freckles and excess water that had clearly spilt everywhere as if he had just run a marathon and, in a panicked frenzy, poured a whole bottle of water over his head.

"Nah. Got Kia Ora in my bag," I responded, trying to keep my cool. But inside, I was fuming. The other boys also looked annoyed at the interruption by the fat turd. Kevin lazily leaned all his weight on the water fountain near the classroom and watched us. It felt good that I wasn't the only one struggling with this burden of social ineptitude. A small sense of solidarity grew among us boys at that moment. Alex smiled and lent back down to continue the rhyme.

"IT'S TOO ORANGEY FOR CROWS!" chuckled Kevin loud enough so everyone in the playground would stop and hear his clear genius.

I made the mistake of looking up and retracting my foot, which, in turn, caused Alex to miss count and once again threw the whole selection process out of whack. I glared with the fire of a thousand suns as I watched Kevin's waxwork flabby face form a smug and arrogant smile. His jowls stretched long, and he squeezed his chungs back with delight, as if he thought knowing and reciting the stupid, nonsensical Kia Ora advert jingle was tantamount to rocket science. Next, I watched as Kevin went in for another drink. I saw how he squeezed his thick, slug-like lips around the nozzle. I looked on in horror as he sucked tight-ishly hanging on the pump tap with two short piggy fingers. I hated this kid, and at that moment I fantasised of walking over there, grabbing his head tight in a head lock, holding it still, using my other hand to peg his nose shut and operating the tap lever with my knee till his head exploded like a gigantic hairy water balloon, and his body flopped dead to the ground. I even saw and heard the words, "Fatality", ring overhead within my pleasant daydream in the style of Mortal Kombat.

"Michael. Come on, mate." Alex motioned for me to put my leg back in the middle.

"Sorry," I apologised as I regained my bearings on where I was and what was going on.

"Ip, dip, dog shit, you are…" Alex continued till the point he couldn't speak over the din of the heavyset, flat-footed steps that were quickly approaching. As the footsteps slowed down, we knew exactly what was going on. We huddled in closer to each other trying desperately to build a wall around us with our combined backs. Regrettably, in order to conduct an accurate selection rhyme, Alex was forced to bend down to knee level, leaving a disastrously large gap in our wall. Kevin peeked his snout in and over and saw what was going on.

"Can I play?" Kevin shouted.

We all closed our eyes in pain as the sound collectively shook our cochleas to kingdom come.

Sam spoke first coming up with what, we thought, to the IQ of a Kevin, sounded like a reasonable excuse. "It's really more of a four-man game… Sorry," Sam said, smiling to take some of the sting out of it. He was good like that.

Kevin, wasn't having any of it.

"Nonsense," Kevin roared. "Look, I'll be it," he shrieked.

"Fine!" said Alex…

We all looked at each other quickly, then suddenly darted off in different directions.

Kevin, who had forgotten to pay attention to who actually had their feet in and, evidently, had no clue as to what we were even playing pulled away and then charged over to what he assumed was a sitting duck. A moment later, Adam Daniels was hit by the runaway freight train that was Kevin, knocking him into the wall of Miss Butterworth's office. Kevin again slammed into him, this time kissing Adam repeatedly on the cheeks, pausing in between each kiss only to state, "You're it, you're it," sounding more and more winded each time. It was like watching the beginnings of a gay child porn rape scene.

Adam, completely humiliated by this point and stinking of Kevin's presumably hot breath, pushed Kevin away and began to cry. Sam, Alex, Steven and myself fell about laughing as the break time monitor seized Kevin by the scruff of the neck and pulled him inside for the remainder of the break. Sadly, the end of break whistle soon sounded much too soon, and we had little time in which to salvage one game of stuck in the mud. But, in return, we had all had the pleasure of watching Kevin get served a good dose of justice. This was a fair consolation prize.

As we re-entered the classroom after break, everyone took their place on the floor making sure to avoid the piss stain on the carpet left earlier from Richard Slate's pathetic excuse for a bladder. I took a moment to have a private word with the teacher. I asked her if it were possible to have Kevin sat at the far back of the class away from everyone else for the safety of everyone's hearing. Miss Lily tried to explain to me that, whilst this was a good idea from a practical standpoint, it wouldn't go down well from an ethical point of view. She started talking about a potential uprising by Kevin's parents, dropping names like Rosa Parks and MLK as metaphors. I argued with her that racial and practical segregation had nothing to do with each other. She mentioned something about Kevin and special needs, I responded, "We're all gonna have special needs when we can't hear anything!" I tried desperately to reason with her about the greater good, the death of one to spare millions etc. etc. but she had final say and couldn't be swayed despite how rational my arguments were.

I was just about to take my seat on the ground when Miss Lily announced that we would be joining Mrs Rose's group for a movie as a treat on our first day. We all marched into Class One where we were joined by the initial children we had been cleaved from at the start of the day, when Miss Lily had called out our names from her proverbial Schindler's list, sparing us from trivialities of these idiots. I spied my mates in the kerfuffle of the two classes mixing and sat down between Sam and Steve. Across the room, the Class One children who had clearly selected their friendship groups (whether through deliberate choice or natural selection), sat quietly looking on at us second graders with a dumbfounded, gormless stare, like a deer caught in headlights. Whether this look was due to their collective stupidity or it was merely the look they always wore as a default to any slight break in their equilibrium brought on by momentary confusion, I'll never know. Happily, Kevin mindlessly found his way over to the Class One group and sat down next to Ben Fields, who was nervously scratching his head and sniffing his fingers. Next, Ben Fields began to pluck at a hole in his trouser crotch he had managed to create in the short space between the beginning of the day and now. To Ben Field's left sat Rebecca Trout, who would soon be known as the school bitch (at least in my eyes). Rebecca Trout was whispering to Amy Price (another girl whose attitude would piss me off beyond measure in future times). Behind Ben Field, Rebecca Trout and Amy Price, Daniel Parker leaned in to join the girls' conversation then let out a quiet girlish giggle. Already I knew I didn't like him. Next to Amy Price, sprawled, slovenly out and taking up a gigantic piece of real estate on the Class One carpet like a human Jabba-the-Hut was Beverly Walters, who was busy picking her nose and eating its contents. From behind Beverly Walters, as though out of nowhere, Darren Bisset's silly little head popped up and his eyes quickly and sharply scanned the horizon like a bewildered meerkat. On seeing Mrs Rose, Darren Bisset rose too, and he strolled over to her and handed over a video tape. It was Ghostbusters. Darren Bisset had brought it from home for us to watch, and he proudly announced this fact like he had the cure for cancer. A simple smile stretched across his face as he waited for applause that never came, then, eventually, he took his seat. Oddly, Darren Bisset was the only one not wearing the school uniform and, instead, was wearing a black tracksuit with a cartoon man wheeling a massive motorbike on the front. *It looked pretty sweet,* I thought to myself, but soon came to realise that wearing that tracksuit was probably as good and sophisticated as it got for poor Darren Bisset. He was, otherwise, without a doubt the dumbest kid on the planet. Academically speaking, he was brain dead. If IQs could go into the negatives then…well you get my point. Still, he was nice enough and that pleasant, not threatening, affable attitude has served him well in life, helping him gain a job in a warehouse in Cirencester hauling junk. So it's nice to know at least he's achieved his potential in the most logical field for him, simple repetitive manual labour.

As soon after Ghostbusters ended, the day was finished. Being the first day, it was only a half day, so we ate our lunches, and stood outside waiting for our parents to come pick us up.

To my dismay, everyone seemed to have a cooler lunch box than me. Particularly, the boys in my friendship group. Steve had Thundercats, Alex had Sonic, a new kid who had joined us in the last few minutes of play named Adam Blackburn had a Transformers lunchbox, but Sam Bailey had the pièce de résistance, the magnum opus of lunchboxes: A Teenage Mutant Ninja turtles' lunch box. I looked on with jealousy but also with pride in the good and diligent choice my best friend's mum had made. If lunchboxes were anything to go by (aside from my decapitated Mickey Mouse Head, which I was now performing what could only be described as brain surgery on as I snapped the head open at the top and retrieved my peanut butter and jam sandwiches), we were clearly the A team!

Parents soon began to flock into the schoolyard identifying their younglings and taking them away. Eventually, thirty minutes after the penultimate mum had left with their child, my mum came swanning in without an apology for her lateness. This was standard, as she never considered punctuality a thing to be concerned about (this did and still does annoy me to this day but I've learnt to endure it). As we walked off together, she asked me about my day, as most parents would. I told her about Words and Pictures and finger mouse, about playtime and that insufferable Kevin character and the mistaken game of kiss chase he had initiated, ravishing Adam Daniels. She chuckled as if she'd heard it all before. Finally, she asked what I did after break time.

"We watched Ghostbusters," I said.

"Oh, was it good?" she asked.

"I have no idea," I sighed. "That prick Kevin was talking all the way through it!"

"Oh dear," she said.

Oh dear!? I thought. *Oh dear, indeed!*

Chapter 3
Mrs Lawrence and the
Vandalised Finger Painting

One year later and we had all grown accustomed to our classmates and knew our cliques and place in the year-group hierarchy….all except Kevin, who had still managed not to settle but acted as more of a floater among groups. He probably saw his behaviour as well-rounded, mature and accepted by everybody, but in reality, he was more, 'flying by the seat of his pants on the good nature of groups', till, eventually, they'd grow too weary of his oddball nature and excommunicate him. Then to simply avoid the obviousness of the rejection, he'd move along to another group to try and establish a meaningful role there. Of course, one might think this roundabout and perpetual change could easily be avoided had Kevin lowered his standards and joined the group of rejects (comprising of Ben Fields, Darren Bisset, Beverly Walters and Anthony Telling), but even they had their qualms about him.

It was about quarter past one on a Thursday afternoon. Our class was involved in some Arts and Crafts. We had spent the early part of the morning gathered around the class computer (a BBC Micro) waiting turns to play a spelling game. This was until Michael Swift had cunningly discovered a copy of Chuckie Egg, hidden among the files, which ended up disrupting the whole learning environment by introducing fun into our day. Fun was strictly prohibited during school time and, for his sins, Michael had been sent to Miss Butterworth's office for a bollocking and subsequently Chuckie Egg had been sadly deleted. Now, after lunch, we were using a tub of glue and crap plastic brushes to stick down paper cutouts of shapes on vast A3 sheets of coloured paper. Kevin sat across the table from me and, whilst the class had both been working for thirty industrious minutes, he had accomplished nothing and was instead busying himself sniffing the different pots of glue and chuckling after each sniff. Diagonally opposite me, John Chomsky, the class brain, was sat reclined on his chair having finished five minutes earlier and was presently tucking into his sleeve like he hadn't eaten in days. In fairness, Chomsky did possess the look of a starving child: despite growing up in a fairly affluent family, he was consistently emaciated, pale and gaunt looking; you honestly wouldn't be able to pick him out of a line up at Auschwitz. I personally blamed this on the fact that he was a very fussy eater. I had once brought him around to dinner one evening at my house, and he had worked my mum up into a real huff as he declined or poo-pooed literally everything she offered to make him for dinner, even turning down pudding (a cherry pie) because he simply didn't like cherries. Needless to say, that was the first and last time he came round to the Sleggs' residence. In hindsight, perhaps if we had served up a plate of sleeves, he would have been more tempted to dine.

Back in class, I had finished sticking on my shapes and had begun the next phase of the project: finger painting. I took to the task adequately, but I was no Da Vinci. My attempt to draw the four Ninja Turtles and Splinter left much to be desired but I didn't care. For me, school was merely a chore and doing my work to the worst of my ability was standard fare. Saying that, since I was painting the Ninja Turtles, I did feel a deeper sense of pride and responsibility in my task than I, otherwise, would have done due to my growing fondness towards these particular fictional characters. Respectively, Chomsky had decorated his finger-painting collage with Daleks (his passion in life that no one else in the class shared much less understood), and Matthew Smith, the class 'palaeontologist wannabe', had branded his work of art with crudely drawn triceratops and pterodactyls.

It was getting on to 2 pm, and Arts and Crafts was winding up. Most of us had handed in our projects to Mrs Lawrence and were now clearing away scraps of paper and cotton wool buds into the recycling. Kevin, on the other hand, who had seemingly been caught up in a day dream for the past fifteen minutes, was leant back on his chair unknowingly testing the weight limit of the two back prong legs to the limit, whilst a single line of drool made its way down his chin. In the past hour, I had not seen him lift a finger which, given the projects we were working on, was more than ironic.

Mrs Lawrence began to hover around the table peering on at the remaining stragglers' work.

"What's that?" enquired Lawrence, pointing at a few badly painted wavy lines covering Ben Fields' A3 poster.

"A fart," giggled Ben.

"I see," Lawrence replied with a long sigh and she rolled her eyes as though the child's fate had been sealed long ago.

Mrs Lawrence moved on to look over Michael Swift who looked deep in thought as he finished off the last few strokes of his masterpiece.

"Done," he yelled, as Mrs Lawrence looked down on the finger painting adorning his poster. At first, she struggled to make it out and was forced to lift her glasses up from the end of her nose right to the top. It was at this point the image focused in, and she saw three stick figures. One was stabbing another whilst the third lay down on the ground with a headstone marking RIP.

Cautiously, Lawrence asked: "What's happening here?"

Michael Swift beamed with pride and looked back at Lawrence with a hint of madness in his eyes. "Well, let me tell you. This is me. I'm stabbing Mrs Butterworth, and that lying in the grave is you. I used a Saracen sword to slay you with because that's my favourite type of sword."

Lawrence gulped. "Blimey," she spoke under her breath seemingly unsure about whether to give him another bollocking. After all, the painting was one of the most clear and well-presented ones in the class, and Michael had clearly not learned anything about school conduct from his previous bollocking earlier that day. Eventually, Lawrence moved on down the table and was stopped in her tracks as she glared over Kevin's canvas. Kevin, still idly leaning back on his chair, jumped as Lawrence shrieked at him:

"What is the meaning of this!?!"

Kevin abruptly wiped the drool from his chin and awoke with the snort of a dishevelled pig. He glanced down at his paper to see a collage of…of…Well it really wouldn't be appropriate to put down in print, in detail, in this book what he saw. Suffice it to say it was definitely X-rated material. There was no confusion as to who was pictured in this obscene rendition either. Branded into the page at the bottom were the words, 'Mrs Lawrence.' The longer Lawrence stared at this horrifying artwork, the wider her eyes got.

Kevin in the meantime stuttered and stammered in fear, "I didn't do it, Mrs Lawrence," he cried.

In fairness, I could have attested to his innocence as I had watched him for the past hour while the afternoon away in a dream land of his own, not once doing a lick of work. However, whoever had framed him had been smart and had clearly understood how heavily Kevin could daydream. To this end, they had (unbeknownst to Kevin) dipped Kevin's fingers in the appropriate colours as Kevin had, eyes glazed, indulged in delusions of grandeur like being elected President of the United States or performing some crazy Evel-Knievel stunt to a sell-out crowd.

Abruptly, Mrs Lawrence flipped Kevin's hands over and, on discovering the paint daubs on his fingers, lifted him up by the scruff of the neck (a manoeuvre that he was so accustomed to he moved with it to reduce the tug) and marched him to Mrs Butterworth's office clutching the A3 piece of artwork as she went. "What's that about?" asked Richard Slate, as the picture passed by, not understanding the ins and the outs of the birds and the bees. We all laughed at him, of course, which, in turn, caused the usual circle of human drama where he cried, and we had to hush him up before Mrs Lawrence got back. This was a tiresome and unnecessarily repetitive exercise for us boys of St Paul's School. It annoyed the hell out of us that Slate's parents had raised such a pussy, and we were left to deal with the consequences of that.

At the end of the day, we discovered Kevin's mum had been called in for a special meeting on appropriate child behaviour with Mrs Butterworth and been given a warning which included the words, 'child services', 'special school' and 'institution' amongst others. All the while Kevin protested his innocence and for once he actually was. I should have felt guilty keeping my silence, but this felt like a dose of long overdue karma and who was I to stand in the way of that? The situation was made all the more amusing to me later that evening as I lay in bed and recalled

Mrs Lawrence telling us the basis of the Arts and Crafts project that afternoon. Her words echoed in my mind:

"Alright, class. I want you to do a collage of finger painting of your favourite things."

A small cackle left my lips, and I closed my eyes with a wry smile on my face. A smile that said, "Well done, Sleggsy. Good job. You got away with it."

Chapter 4
The Longest Day: Part 1

A few years had passed since the incident with the finger painting, and I had had a brief respite from Kevin's boorish behaviour for at least one of those as he was held back a year to accommodate for his astonishing ineptitude to keep up with the class's learning. That had all changed this year, however, as in an effort to keep students from falling behind, the school had brought in a new initiative which consolidated two-year groups into the same class and toned down the overall difficulty of the academia for each class. This was a comfortable change for most students like me as it just meant we didn't have to work too hard to obtain top marks as the benchmark was lowered in turn, and since I was in school to socialise foremost, not to learn, I enjoyed the easier more laid-back pace. On the other end of the scale, boffins who for some bizarre reason enjoyed work, like John Day, found it frustrating and limiting, but they were soon moved up a year to accommodate for their impatience and Carl Sagan level IQs. That too was a bit of a blessing as John Day was a difficult boy to work with as he possessed an arrogance and level of patronising that was unbecoming of a nine-year-old, even towards the teachers. You would think seeing the back of his hydrocephalic sized cranium would be cause for celebration; however, in his absence, our class had proverbially robbed Peter to pay Paul and re-adopted Kevin. The black sheep was back into our clean pasture and regardless of the new 'toned down' learning curriculum he still dragged behind like a dead dog on a lead.

It was around 2 pm, and we were returning from a very short lived P.E class which was cancelled thanks to an over excited Patrick McDougal punting a sponge football at the ceiling, almost as soon as we entered the gym, which immediately hit the lighting cover of a strip light sending it to the floor and shattering it to smithereens. This was annoying as up until P.E the day had been a real ball buster, and this was the one class that I could genuinely enjoy. Today was meant to be apparatus day, which in P.E terms was like winning the lottery or landing on the Y bird stop in an episode of Playdays. On the plus side, we all had front row seats to watch Miss Smith explode at Patrick for his stupid act and send him to the Headmistress's office for a further bollocking. I think what cracked me up the most was the change of pure elation to utter fear in Patrick's face in the space of a microsecond, at the drop of a hat, or in this case, a lighting cover. This pleasure was short lived as we were soon herded back to class like prisoners in the gulag heading out to the fields for an extra hour of unplanned work. To make it easy on herself, Miss Smith simply issued us a premade A4 page of maths problems, presumably kept in her desk for such an emergency as this.

This sucked as my day had been in the shitter from 9 a.m. The first 3 hours were taken up by Slate and his special needs lady giving us a lecture on his disability (short sightedness), explaining the ins and outs of the eye and his need for his thick glasses which made it look like he was about to go scuba diving. Of course, Richard attempted to milk the sympathy out of the class from the very first minute saying outlandish things like, "Yeah, being short sighted is no joke, I could have died when I was born!" I think I was the only one in the class to stare back at him with a look of utter impatience for his impudence and question his thin logic and clear use of hyperbole as I repeated, "You nearly died from being born because you were short sighted?"

Richard maintained his resolve, "Yep!" he replied, confidently, hoping I wouldn't take such a touchy subject further and expose him for the mass-market bullshit seller he was. His hopes were misplaced.

"How?" I asked, beaming back. Richard crumbled and not being able to come up with a legitimate answer he resorted to his usual fall back, crying. Of course, this was followed by me getting told off by the teacher for my 'lack of understanding with such a sensitive subject'. I did my best to argue my way out of trouble saying, "Yes, I do have a lack of understanding, I lack to understand how being born short sighted can cause you to die.

You don't die from being short sighted, you just don't. I'm not stupid," but the teacher just couldn't see my point.(ironically). I had no problem with Richard peddling his ailments on stage in order to elicit sympathy from the class, but I did have a problem with being fed lies and calling it learning. With all the medical shit I had endured up to that point, I felt like one of those American soldiers calling out idiot civilians in military gear walking around Malls pretending they served. To be fair though, at the time, I didn't really care about the whole 'stolen valour' thing, I just wanted to watch Richard squirm as the class had already endured 2 and a half hours of watching him smugly piss his pants with pride with all the focus on him and his crap short sightedness and goggle eyes. Alas, for my sins, I was remanded to the back seat of the class, and spent the next lesson trying desperately to view the TV screen from behind 20 of my peers' heads as we all watched a program called Earth Warp about an alien named Ollie. This TV watching was made all the more difficult as Gene Colins who was sitting near the front kept raising his glasses off above his head and into the air every 2 minutes to inspect them, blow on them and clean them a ridiculously unnecessary amount of times. He had just got them that morning and clearly found them fascinating, and in a way raised them above his head in order to show off his new toy to the rest of the class, much to the chagrin of the pupils sitting behind him. By the 12th or 13th time, this act had run its course and the odd student jumped in by yelling, "Gene!" to which he'd quickly jolt back and put his immensely clean glasses back on his face. In his defence, Gene did get bullied a lot, and I guess he thought, at least these new glasses thing will make him somewhat interesting and give him a talking point for a day or so.

Thoughts of this day's events plus a lacklustre snack and lunchtime, tossed around my head for a moment as I went to my assigned seat just outside the classroom in the auxiliary seating area to tackle my sheet of maths problems. Opposite me sat Kevin Blankenhorn with his support teacher. Kevin's glazed eyes peered at his sheet for a moment, then he began to write down answers. Wrong answers but answers all the same. Ironically, this wasn't what his support teacher picked up on. As she glanced at his paper, which was now littered with numbers made up of straight horizontal and vertical lines with tiny spaces in between she asked:

"Why are you writing like that?"

"I'm writing in calculator font 'cos it looks cool," Kevin huffed, concentrating ever so hard as his tongue hung heavy out of his mouth.

"But it's such a slow and tedious way of writing," she chuckled, trying to take the sting out of the underlying annoyance in her voice. Kevin didn't respond. His support teacher took a big breath as if she was going to say something, but then paused, and let out a big sigh, like she knew this was not a battle she was going to win. These trivialities were a daily occurrence, a tale as old as time and like all people running up a hill she had grown weary and ground down. She collapsed into her hand for support, her elbow on the table, and began tapping her fingers on her cheek, occasionally glancing over at me for sympathy. That day, however, I had none to give. Earlier that morning, I had found out my mother and Kevin's mother had conspired against me and organised a play date for the two of us at his house. I still remember the heated car ride into school that morning as my mum broke the news to me in the same style she had done so many times before when telling me I required another heart surgery. The shock and anger was no less severe. This felt like a massive betrayal of trust which was only made worse when I went to my dad for support only to have him side with my mum. I felt like Julius Caesar muttering, "Et tu, Brutus?" as he was being stabbed to death by both his enemies and comrades. As I pondered on my after-school dilemma finishing the last of the maths problems, I looked up to see Kevin's husky face panting heavily and staring gormlessly at me like a boxer dog with cataracts.

"Cheer up, Michael. You're coming over mine after school to play," he woofed, his chungs swaying in the aftermath of his words.

"Yep, I'm aware of the arrangement, Kevin, thank you," I answered back, knowing this was the icing on the bullshit cake I had spent the whole day eating. I glanced back down at the table just to avoid eye contact in a vain attempt to keep my composure.

"I've got you all evening, till 7:30," Kevin said deviously, following it up with a sinister slow chuckle. I quickly looked up shocked, it was as if he already knew this was going to be a nightmare for me and was taunting me with his temporary power hold.

The final school bell tolled and I gulped. For the next few hours, Kevin would have the home advantage, I was on his territory and all bets were off. As we both waited in the school playground for his mum to arrive, dark thoughts clouded and raced through my mind of what would be in store for me that evening. However, what I eventually saw and now know went way beyond any of my most awful and strange predictions…

Chapter 5
The Longest Day: Part 2

Kevin and I had both been waiting in the playground for about 15 minutes, and it had started to rain. Eventually, a gangly looking woman with what looked like severe meth mouth popped her head around the school gate. Her lanky body soon followed along. At least, initially she looked lanky but on closer inspection seemed to hold an odd beer belly and muffin tops that shaped out her brown corduroy sweater. She wore a raincoat; she was the only one wearing a raincoat! She wandered over to us and began to speak.

"Hello Michael, I'm Pam, Kevin's mum. You're coming over to ours this afternoon."

"Yeah, I know!" I said back, very matter-a-factly.

She went to shake my hand, her massive masculine hands completely engulfed my child-sized hand, and she squeezed it so tight I swear I felt a bone break.

"Come along then you two. Car's just out the front," she said, ruffling Kevin's hair with her banana fingers, which then get caught in a knot as she pulled away. Kevin squealed and recoiled like an alley cat who'd been booted, and we both followed her out into the street. As we approached the car, a brown/grey rusty station wagon, Pam ran off ahead of us having just spotted a parking attendant putting a ticket on her car. As Kevin and I caught up, there was a lot of yelling and use of language I hadn't heard up until that point in my life, but instinctively knew it wasn't appropriate for our young ears. After a lot more shouting, verbal profanity and naughty hand gesturing, the conflict eventually ended. Whether it had been resolved or not was anyone's guess at this point. Kevin helped himself to the shotgun seat. As he got in, Pam turned around, looked at me and said:

"Your chariot awaits my liege."

She even bowed and swung her arm in a pointing manner towards the door. I think it was a poor attempt at humour, but I wasn't laughing; my good nature already at its wits end, and I knew this was gonna be a long night! As I opened the backseat passenger door, an avalanche of empty Pepsi cans, crisp packets, beer bottles, dog kibble, receipts and numerous other wrappers and junk tumbled out onto the street and got blown around by the prevailing wind.

"Don't mind the rubbish, Michael, just push that stuff to the other side of the seat."

"Right," I sighed, as I climbed into what looked like the back of a refuse truck. I literally couldn't even see the seat I was sitting on.

"I keep meaning to clean this car out, but yunno how it is," Pam remarked. The smell in the car was that of rotting apple core, animal faeces and cat pee. I felt around for the window winder for fear of vomiting. I guided my hand past used tissues, and Trio wrappers, and reached the spot where the winder should have been. It was missing.

"Window's broken, sorry Michael," sighed Pam. We still hadn't left the parking spot, Pam seemed to be having some problems with the transmission.

"Window's broken, and so am I…" I heard her whisper as she took the hood down from her rain jacket revealing her straw like hair. Her voice was broken like someone on the verge of tears. I saw her haystack head bob up and down, and she tried to start the car again, this time to a successful rumble. Pam took a big sniff and regained her composer as we pulled away and left Gloucester Street.

About ten minutes later, we arrived at Kevin's house, Kevin was sipping the last out of a calypso drink. It wasn't a fresh one, just the remnant of one he had found in the foothold of his front seat. Kevin's house was standard council fare, with the porridge oat looking grey pebble-dash walls on the outside, and a broken fence that hung from one hinge that inconveniently meant lifting it and pulling it each time you walked through it. In the front garden, upon the layer of overgrown crab grass and sporadic weed infestations lay a cheap, rusty, climbing frame on its side. The cement pathway which ran down the middle was littered with bike parts and naked GI Joes.

Kevin and I waited outside for what seemed like an eternity in the pouring rain as Pam pottered around in the boot of her car, layering herself up with hundreds of Tesco carrier bags (full of microwave meals, choc ices, crisps and blocks of Tesco value lard) that hung like Christmas decorations all around her. Alas! there was no angel at the top of this Christmas tree. I offered to help carry some bags to speed the process up, but she quickly declined any of my help; meanwhile, Kevin stood idly by panting like a dog as if the brisk walk up the garden path had worn him out. His shirt was now fully untucked, and he was fiddling with his belly button, pulling out bits of crusty dry skin from its inner depths. Eczema most likely. Finally, Kevin's mum arrived at the door.

"Piss off!" she screamed at Kevin, then gave him a little kick, as he was standing directly in her way. I looked at Pam in shock, she looked back in contempt, it was clearly too late in the day for her to contain her bravado of a nice mum, and she was too tired to masquerade any shame. She shoved the key into the lock angrily, it got jammed, and she quickly lost her temper again.

"Blasted door," I heard her mutter under her breath. Eventually, with a little jiggle and a kick, the door swung open. Pam quickly waddled, heavy laden to the kitchen table and put down the layers of Tesco bags in a big pile.

The kitchen floor was white linoleum with black diamond shapes interspersed to make a primitive, basic pattern. The first thing I noticed when I entered the Blankenhorn premises is that almost immediately, my shoe had walked on something sticky on the kitchen floor. I quickly deduced, however, that this wasn't an isolated incident as, in fact, both my shoes had seemed to have found a sticky spot on the floor. More than just an unlucky coincidence, it soon became apparent that, in fact, the entire floor was sticky, and most likely, not been cleaned in years.

Kevin and I moved into the living room where the fireplace was crackling its last flames. In front of it, lay asleep a very old, unhealthy looking dog. His hair was missing in tufts among his body as if he had been exposed to some nuclear fallout. Kevin walked up to him and gave him a little stroke on the head, which by its sheer friction took off a good handful of hair. In the commotion the dog awoke, and quickly went about nibbling its body, almost chewing off his own leg, presumably riddled with fleas. I felt sorry for the poor bastard. He looked like he hadn't been walked in years, let alone let out in the garden to play. Kevin scratched his head and sniffed his fingers.

In the corner of the room, a scrawny kitten vomited, and the dog got up and began to lick it up, as if this was the standard sad circle of life. Next, the sound of a hamster wheel interrupted the momentary silence. I looked over to see a hamster cage full to the wheel of faeces and sodden sawdust that had simply been layered on top of older soiled sawdust instead of cleaned out regularly. The Wheel was the last bastion of high ground. Of course, there was no food to be seen in its food dish, and its water bottle was dry as a bone. This angered me greatly. At this point, I turned my head to bollock Kevin about the poor state of the animals when, just as I turned, a massive gust of wind and soot blew into my face. I coughed, spluttered and blinked my way through the smog till, eventually, my eyes zeroed in on what had just happened. Kevin was standing there tittering to himself holding out the wood fire puffer. I was facing the end of the barrel and had just received a shot to the face. Quickly, I rubbed the soot off my face and snatched the puffer from his clutches almost pushing him into the fireplace in the tussle. Part of me secretly wanted to, but I was too smart and knew that even my young age wouldn't get me off in court for manslaughter with the 'we were just play fighting' defence. Besides my parents knew my true feelings about Kevin and you can be sure as shit they'd testify against me. No, unfortunately, I was still a guest in someone's house and years of careful etiquette indoctrination on 'how to behave as a guest at someone else's house' by my parents kept my actions stuck in limbo between a rock and a hard place. I laid the puffer down next to the fireplace, gritted my teeth, sucked in all my hatred, sighed, regained my composer and asked Kevin:

"What shall we do?"

Kevin was still giggling to himself at his asinine prank but beginning to calm down. His face which was beetroot red was now a slightly more normal peach colour, though I knew it would go to a dullish grey before long as that was his usual complexion, (I'm sure due to an unhealthy vitamin deficiency in his diet of crisps and E number riddled drinks).

"Wanna watch *The Terminator*?" he puffed, his breath returning.

I couldn't believe it, I had actually wanted to see The Terminator since I had first heard about it. I had no idea what it was about, but I knew it was one of those naughty 18 rated films with lots of violence and swearing, that I wasn't usually privy too. Of course, at that point, I wasn't aware of pornos, so films with excessive violence and swearing were as bad as they got to the best of my knowledge and just the simple act of watching them made me feel hard as nails. I could also add it to my badge of honour in the playground to gain respect from my friends. 'Course, I couldn't let them know where I watched it as that would either negate the coolness I had just earned, or even worse, boost Kevin's coolness in the school playground, and I did not want him climbing the social ladder even one step. I hated him too much for that.

"Yeah alright," I replied nonchalantly like I could take it or leave it.

"It's upstairs, come on, we'll watch it in my room," he replied, and we went out of the living room, which by that point I was sure was beginning to rot and felt like the upside down in Stranger Things. We climbed the stairs slowly, Kevin leading the way. We only got half way when Kevin decided he had had enough. He paused for a moment puffing like he was having some kind of asthma attack.

"No, it's no good. I'm gonna have to get a drink," he wheezed, as I got slammed against the wall on the 5th step as he squeezed his wide frame past me and scurried down the stairs towards the kitchen. *For crying out loud, I was the one with the heart condition, and you don't see me practically keeling over on a simple set of stairs*, I thought to myself as I stood there. I was about to sit down on the step when I noticed that the step, covered in a carpet that had worn so thin that you could see the original wood underneath, was pancaked with patches of fox shit and biscuit crumbs that had probably been there since the Blankenhornes moved in. There was no banister to lean on, and the wall had that uncomfortable scratchy/bubble speckle to it, so leaning against that really wasn't an option either. There was a rusty nail hanging out of the wall, presumably a family portrait once hung there but there was no sign of it now. I stared at the nail for a moment pensively. Then annoyed by its lack of use and ugly 'out of place' nature I tugged it out of the wall. The wall crumbled away a little making obvious but not major cracks in the surrounding area like a spider web branching out a few centimetres in multiple directions. Quickly I put the nail back and shot up to the top of the stairs. Kevin yelled, from the kitchen.

"Want some Ribena, Mike?"

"Yes, please," I answered, rubbing my fingers together to get rid of the last of the wall dust, like I was escaping from Shawshank. I stood on the landing for a good two minutes till Kevin came back around from the kitchen at the bottom of the stairs. The two minutes had given me time to observe and analyse my surroundings. To my left was the bathroom. A ring of scum encircled the bathtub. There was a novelty 'Ed the duck' shampoo dispenser that was squeezed dry and open on the side of the tub. Next to it sat the remains of an orange piece of soap. The taps had one of those old rubber shower converters stuck to it, the type that is basically two interconnected hoses that syphon into one pissy end that doesn't really work due the weak water pressure of the tap water and gravity required to actually have a shower. Next to the bathtub was the toilet; its lid missing and its seat hanging off. On closer inspection, I'm sure I would have seen a floater that had simply refused to go down for months. Below, at the bottom neck of the toilet lay wrapped around a towel, presumably mopping up leakage from a broken cistern. The sink was in the corner and the cheap knock off porcelain bowl was slathered with dry spat out toothpaste stains, and a little blood and dirt. On the windowsill, above the sink stood a bottle of what looked like Second World War Iodine, its label was bleached over and its neck was all crusty. Next to that lay a used toothpaste dispenser. It had been squeezed to capacity, and was for all intents and purposes empty, save for a little residue that had run from the open end to the floor of the windowsill, which had dried and stuck in place. A collection of cardboard toilet paper centres were stacked untidily in the corner of the windowsill. The bin below the sink was full and overflowing. In short, the bathroom, as it stood, was in complete disrepair and reminded me of pictures of ghost town houses where people had just left suddenly due to a nuclear meltdown, like Chernobyl.

Next, I briefly gazed into Pam's room. Not much there but a dresser (and a black pair of underwear that hung from the handle), a gaudy mirror, some make up, a box of condoms, some money, a glass ashtray that was overflowing in cigarette butts, a double bed mattress, covered in black satin sheets and two grimy windows with sleazy white netted curtains hanging off to the side.

As Kevin puffed his way back up the stairs, spilling a good portion of Ribena onto the paper-thin carpet with each step he trudged, I forced one of those 'happy to see him' smiles. I wasn't happy to see him, I was happy to watch the Terminator though, so I was willing to play the game. Kevin was one step shy of the landing when he tripped spilling the remainder of the glass (I say glass but I really mean a blue and green plastic cup… the type they'd usually give kids in reception class or Sunday school to drink juice out of at the end) of Ribena over me as he lost his balance.

"Oh Kevin!" I rebuked.

"Sorry," he scoffed, taking responsibility but surmounting it to comic clumsiness as if it excused him. This annoyed me more. Straight away, he drank the remainder of his cup and led me into his room.

Kevin's room was dark. His main light bulb was missing, he had grey wallpaper, and a small pokey window in the centre. Clothes were strewn everywhere, and an undressed mattress on the floor faced a small 14-inch wood-panelled TV set. On top of the TV sat a cheap Alba VCR.

"Bit dark in here," I remarked.

"Hang on," Kevin replied, sprawling out on the mattress then crawling his way towards a lamp at the far end. A small click and there was light. Kevin scavenged around through a myriad of VHS tapes that lay sloppily by tossing aside tapes that weren't marked, 'The Terminator'. Eventually, he found it, but I was surprised by his deciphering capabilities as 'Terminator' was written 'Turmanater' almost illegibly on the face of the tape in tippex that had run horribly at the time of writing and was chipping ever since. He jammed it into to the VCR and began to play the tape. The movie came on, it was fuzzy but workable. I lay down on the mattress on my stomach next to Kevin as we both supported our heads with our forearms, our elbows sinking into the mattress.

About 40 minutes in, aside from hearing Kevin yawn and fart 5 or 6 times and scratch his ass under his grey, polyester school trousers an innumerable amount of times, I was enjoying the movie. Suddenly, without warning, Kevin wrapped his arm around my neck and pulled tightly rolling at the same time and taking me with him off the mattress.

"Come on, Michael, let's wrestle," he shouted like a giddy kid right into my ear. His breath stank.

"No, I want to watch The Terminator," I retorted in a funny suffocated voice that came about due to the strangulation.

"It's boring, come on!" Kevin barked back tightening his grip.

Furious, I grabbed his arm from my neck and swung it around twisting it into a backward arch that had him hunched over. Next I kneed him in the chest and then let go as his limp fat body collapsed to the floor. He spent a couple of minutes catching his breath, in the meanwhile I regained my prominent position on the mattress and resumed the film. A minute or so passed and I glanced over to where I left Kevin heaped on the floor like dirty laundry, only he wasn't there. Before I could turn my head to scan the room further, a hand grabbed the back of my head by the hair and started pounding my head into the mattress. Then Kevin did the most stupid thing of all. He grabbed his VCR and attempted to slam it on my head. I don't think he realised at the time how severe this could be and could potentially kill me with the impact, as in his child like brain, it was all just childish wrestling. Fortunately, as the VCR came down towards me, it also swung by its cables (still attached at the back) into the front of the TV screen missing my head by a mere few inches.

"Right, that does it," I yelled, springing back into action and giving Kevin an almighty punch in the testicles.

"OOOFFFFHHHH," the impact hit Kevin hard, and I watched him, almost in slow motion, like a tree falling over, kneel to the floor. He lay there motionless for a while save for the rising and falling of his belly in time with his breathing. I expect he wanted me to edge closer to check he was okay so that he could initiate a surprise counter attack, but I wasn't in the mood to check on his wellbeing even if he was actually hurt.

I walked over to the one dingy window in his room and looked outside. It was steamed up, so I used a shirt I found on the floor nearby to wipe it clean. Outside it was getting dark and still raining. The full moon provided some light over the desolate landscape of lower-class back gardens among the neighbourhood. The majority of them were overgrown and had random defunct sofas and appliances in them. I peered down at Kevin's and saw what at first looked like an allotment patch for growing vegetables taking up the lion's share of the garden. I stared at it a little longer and noticed little crosses made from ice lolly sticks, and the backs of those things they put in plant pots to identify flower types. Curiously, I wondered to myself for a minute as to what this was. On the windowsill I found a pair of binoculars. The glass was smudged and there was a sticky substance aligning the peepholes. I cleaned this off with the same shirt I had used to wipe the window with, then dropped it to the floor beside me. Looking through the binoculars I inspected the garden thoroughly. I soon became aware that these crosses were part of an immense pet graveyard that almost took over the entirety of the back garden. Each cross was complete with the pet's name, and date of death written on a corresponding card. There were hundreds of them. As I thought longer on the proverbial animal Arlington cemetery I was witnessing, a dark cold wind howled at the window as if ominously it knew what I was thinking. I couldn't breathe. Kevin's house was a death camp for animals. It seemed they were being farmed in and farmed out just as quick. Once an animal crossed the Blankenhorn threshold, there was no escape. I gulped and took a step back, my eyes wide with fear. I felt like Bruce Willis at the end of the movie 'Unbreakable' when he finds out that Samuel L Jackson is the architect of all the attacks. I turned my head towards Kevin who was still lying on his mattress pretending to be out cold. There was a flash of lightening followed by a clap of thunder and the lamp light went out leaving Kevin's room in complete darkness, save for the moonlight peering through the window.

"Kids, dinner's ready!" Pam screamed from the distant kitchen. Immediately, Kevin hopped up to attention like Pavlov's dog. He then sprinted out of the door and down the stairs like a madman, ravenous for his dinner. I followed behind at a slower, more normal pace. I arrived in the kitchen a few moments after Kevin who was already sat down and slamming the end of his cutlery into the table, chanting in time, "Food, good, food, good, food, good, food, good," like a scene from Lord of the Flies. He went on and on till Pam placed a bowl of stew in front of him, and he went at it like a starving jackal devoid of any etiquette or table manners. Pam was wearing a very skimpy silk Thai looking dressing gown, which seemed far too small for her. Her belly fat rolled over the central belt and it was so short it hung just over her privates like a mini skirt. Her legs were hairy and manish. I gagged in my mouth, but swallowed it quickly.

"Hope you like stew, Michael!" Pam said proudly as she laid a bowl of brown muck in front of me at the table.

"I bought a bunch of vegetables and potatoes at the farmers market for dirt cheap a few weeks ago, said they were gonna throw them out, otherwise," she continued.

"They were probably throwing them out 'cuz they were rotting," I muttered under my breath.

"But I knew better, I just knew I could make a something out of them," she persisted.

I looked back into the bowl of stew, which was really just a congealed mass of Bisto gravy, (some of the granules still weren't broken down) mixed with a cluster of rotten vegetables. I tried my best to be courteous and thankful. Pam began pouring out two grimy glasses of Tesco value lemonade and placed them in front of us. Returning to the kitchen top counter she placed the bottle back and grabbed her bowl of stew.

"I'll be in the other room watching Corrie if you need anything, otherwise, bon appetite," she said with a warm but desperate smile on her face, before marching out of the kitchen and into the living room. I heard her collapse onto the couch with a thud, and imagined a bloom of dust and stench exploding from its old crusty carcass.

The electricity had returned to the house, and the stark glare of the kitchen strip light reflected uncomfortably into my eyes from the cheap, white chipboard table I was sat at. There was an annoying buzzing coming from the fridge, which every two minutes made a gurgling noise as if it were a giant stomach trying desperately to digest the crap food inside it. Feeling sorry for myself, I ate as much of the dinner as I could, at many points, eating around the fluff and dark patches of the vegetables, which were clearly decomposing as I sat there. Who was I kidding, the entire house was rotting, and I felt at that point infected by it and in my own way decaying along with it. When I got back home, if I got back, I promised myself a thorough deep cleansing shower to rid myself of any trace of the dankness that at this point seemed to be seeping into my very pores.

Ten minutes had gone by and I still found myself playing with my food, mostly in an attempt to run out the clock till home time. I sighed and finally gave up.

"That's it, I'm stuffed," I said, even though I was starving.

"Give it here then," Kevin barked and snatched the bowl out of my hand. He had finished his own bowl almost as soon as it was given to him and for his own credit had been sat quite patiently and quietly for me to finish mine. He seemed glad that bowl was still practically full, as he had been salivating the whole time it had been in my possession, watching the movement of the spoon like an animal angling for some in a not too subtle way. He wolfed down the remainder of my bowl then began licking it clean, finishing by wiping his filthy gravy slathered chops with his sleeve like Tom does after a bowl of milk in a Tom and Jerry cartoon; microscopic stew droplets flew everywhere throughout the kitchen, spattering the walls and peppering the cabinets in tiny speckles.

"MUM! PUDDING!!!" he screamed.

"Yes, darling," a tired voice responded as Pam entered the room again and went to one of the cabinets. She got down on her knees and began to dig like a dog.

"They're in here somewhere," she said as chocolate wrappers and Kit Kat foils blew back from between her legs into a pile behind her as she dug her way through the closet.

"Got 'em."

She strained to her feet and exited the cabinet holding a family pack of Tesco Value crisps.

"What flavour would you like Kevin?" she asked. I found it strange that she didn't offer the guest first but put it behind me as just another thing that was odd about this family.

"Salt and Vinegar," he screamed in delight. She grabbed a bag and threw it at him full pelt. It hit him in the head but he didn't react.

"What flavour would you like, Michael?" Pam asked. At this point, I was finding it a little difficult to read her, I had seen her all day playing hot and cold with Kevin. Was she having a mental breakdown or merely the Queen of Narnia talking to Edmund?

"I'll take Prawn Cocktail," I said without much thought.

"I'll take Prawn Cocktail what?" Pam replied crossly. I couldn't believe it, here was Pam Blankenhorn, mother to four unruly cow-faced, freckled brats, living in a cross between what could only be described as a petting zoo for Stephen King and the crumbling other world of the movie *Coraline*, and she had the gall to call me out on my manners.

"I'll take Prawn Cocktail, please," I resigned, realising no argument at this stage would do me good. Inside I was a volcano of impotent rage. Unlike the Blankenhorn though, I had learnt how and when to keep my mouth shut, when to play the game and when to play my cards.

After I had finished my crisps at a slower than normal pace, I glanced up at the kitchen clock to gage how much time I'd bought, or rather ran down, till my mum picked me up at 7:30 pm. Elated, I saw that the clock now read 7:29 pm. Noticing the movement of my eyes and the excitement in my face, Kevin put two and two together (probably the smartest addition he'd ever done). Desperate to burst my bubble, Kevin chuckled cruelly and said:

"Clock's ten minutes fast."

"You can't wait to go home, can you?" he asked as he looked scornfully into my eyes. Ordinarily, I would have put up a pretence of denial and affection along the lines of 'don't be silly' or 'nah, it's been great fun', but today, I was worn thin to the point where I couldn't even muster a response. Instead, I looked back into Kevin's eyes deeply with contempt, sighed and laid my head on the table. My eyes began to close slowly, like Mufasa in the Lion King as he passed away. Moments later, I was awoken by the sound of a doorbell chime. I bounced to my feet like Popeye when he pops a can of spinach down his gob and skipped with sheer joy to the front door, stopping only to pick up my rucksack and lunchbox. We all congregated in the front hall as

Pam opened the door. My mum stood outside with an umbrella. I ran and clung to her like a little child. Embarrassed, both by the fact that I had not shown my mum such affection since I was a toddler and because it was a clear sign of how desperate I was to get out of the Blankenhorn' house, my mum managed a little bit of polite small talk before I dragged her down the lane towards the car. Kevin used this time to wet-willy me, to which my mum understood quite quickly the annoyance and impatience I was expressing.

"How was he, well behaved?" my mum asked Pam. Meanwhile, Kevin had turned to thumping me in the back.

"Yeah, they both were! Got on like a house on fire, right boys…" Pam replied. My mum and I both glanced at each other with the same 'yeah right' look on our faces. Kevin still thumping me on the back turned to kicking me in the legs. My mum knew I could take him, but also realised this was not the time nor the place and felt proud of my restraint.

"That's enough, Kevin!" Pam chortled, clinging onto the collar of his shirt and dragging him back over the threshold.

"Right, well, we best be off," my mum said kindly. "What do you say, Michael?" she added.

"Thanks for having me!" I replied, simply going through the script like a parrot reciting generic lines to deliver upon prompting.

"Anytime," Pam replied, closing the door behind her. We wandered back down the garden path back to the car in silence. I climbed into the front and watched the house disappear in the distance. I felt like Arnold Schwarzenegger in Predator as the chopper picks him up at the end, and he glances out at the jungle with shell shock from the events of the night before.

My mum broke the silence.

"I'm sorry, Michael. I didn't realise Kevin was that bad," she said softly, truly heartfelt.

After a long pause and Vietnam flashback I responded.

"Mum, you have no idea what I've just been through!"

Chapter 6
The Best Laid Plans of
Lemmings and Pogs

Six months had passed and the recurring nightmares of the ordeal I endured that fateful evening at Kevin's house were finally beginning to fade. It was a new school year, and we had all moved up to Miss Harris' class. Kevin had latched on to a new group of pseudo friends, and it would be a while before he'd come back full circle to pester me for a friendship. I took this opportunity to make the most of my freedom and invest in better mates.

As the year petered on, a new fad started in the school playground, a fad called Pogs. This was a simple game which involved flipping milk bottle caps with the help of a bigger plastic spherical shape cap called a 'Kini'. Every day, after school, kids from around the country would rush to the nearest newsagent to buy a packet of Pogs, mostly for collection in large binders. There was 64 Pogs to a series (except series 1 which had 72), which were growing more and more rare and obsolete to make way for series 2 and newer series 3. The game where you'd slam your Kini on top of a tower of face up Pogs in hopes of flipping the majority of them upside down, thus winning, was either played for sport or for keeps. When played for keeps, the shit got real. Each individual Pog had a different illustration on the front, and they were making the rounds in school like chicken pox. The game was fairly primitive, but it was the collection aspect that really hooked the kid's brain like heroine and became an addiction as aggressive as crystal meth to the children of the schoolyard, myself included. One morning, I was playing an intense battle against a lad named Phil Stone from another class at the tail end of snack time. It was intense because we were playing for keeps and playing against the clock. He was an ugly kid with goofy teeth and usually I wouldn't associate with him, not because he was ugly, but really just because I didn't know him that well. In the years since we've gotten to know each other a little but only after a 20-year absence. His hair is short now, and he no longer wears glasses. At the time, the story takes place though he had blonde-grey curly hair and wore spectacles that looked like they came off one of the 1980s newsroom anchorman, or the guy Simon Bates who used to warn us about a film rating before the movie started. You know the type, thick rimmed, square and large, with very little style awareness. Anyway, I digress. So our game was tied, but there was still a handful of Pogs standing in a tower. Phil was physically perspiring, as he knew it was my turn and the bell was about to toll on the snack break. Then just as the bell rang, my Kini slammed down on the stack of Pogs in perfect alignment and the whole remainder of the stack flipped over. I felt like Michael Jordan scoring a 3-point game clincher on the buzzer. Agitated by this, Phil let out a frustrated "Noooo!!!"

"Sorry mate!" I replied as I grabbed my winnings off the grisly tarmac floor. In fairness, I thought he took defeat well for a kid, a lesser man would have whined about it, and as such I felt compelled to shake his hand and remark, "Good game!" as we both walked the green mile back to class.

As I made my way to the classroom, I briefly inspected my winnings and couldn't believe my luck. I had obtained number 63 which, for some reason, was considered as the rarest Pog in the series, and I knew one investor who would be most interested in its whereabouts. Phil should have known this and not been foolish enough to play it in a game of keeps, but his lack of education and loss was my gain. Back in class, I went to work writing and passing a note to Ben Baker. "I have number 63," the note read. He was one Pog shy of completing his Pog set, and I had the missing piece. Ben saw the note and immediately his eyes lit up with excitement as he knew exactly what it meant. Unfortunately, for Ben, I had no intention of trading with him, not for all the gold in King Solomon's mines, but I wished to make him aware of this power hold I now possessed over him. You see, for the longest time, I had watched Ben grow from being one of my closest friends to becoming a bit of a douche.

He was rather spoilt and got all the video games, trips to Disney world and Pogs he asked for. He was also more blessed than me in the looks department and as such had the girls of our year constantly swooning over him, where I was left in the dust. Okay, I'll admit it now, in hindsight, I think my desire to have this hold over him with the Pog had a lot more to do with petty jealousy than it did anything else. Be that as it may it didn't stop Ben hunting me down at lunchtime pretending again to be all chummy and offering me a fair few offers for the trade. In fairness, a lot of his offers were extremely generous, but I obstinately held my reserve just to watch him suffer. It was time for Ben to realise he could no longer get everything he ever wanted so flippantly. The continual brick wall Ben was hitting against was starting to take its toll on him, and I was loving it. Eventually, he conceded. Then he turned back to me and said: "Alright mate, you win, but can I at least see it?"

"No!" I replied, with a smarmy smile on my face. Then he pulled out that age-old reverse psychology trick that has been the downfall of many a dumbass in the past. I should have been smarter, but alas, that day he played me like a fiddle.

"Ah, I bet you don't even have it," Ben scoffed and went to walk away. So convincing was his pantomime that I immediately backed myself up.

"Yeah I do!" I desperately cried back.

"Prove it!" he exclaimed, motioning with his hands out and shrugging his shoulders in the perfect storm of body language meets words to incite evidence of said object.

"Fine," I sighed and reached into my pocket to pull it out. I should have been smarter. As soon as it was revealed, Ben leapt at me like Gollum for the precious ring hammering me to the ground. We tussled around for a couple of minutes, I had no choice but to squish and crumple the Pog in a final attempt at least to ruin it for Ben as he tried to pry it from my hands. Eventually, he snatched it out of my hand, but it was too late. A shadow of its former glory, it was all bent out of shape, torn at the back and soggy from grass dew. It could no longer be ID'ed for what it once was even by a forensic Pog post-mortem.

"You ruined it!" Cried a bitter Ben Baker, discarding the remnant of its ravaged carcass.

"You ruined it, idiot… I told you I wasn't gonna trade, what's the matter with you," I shouted back seething. I wasn't too mad though truthfully; I was more annoyed that my hold over Ben was cut so short than I was for the loss of the Pog, and, at least, I ruined the Pog enough for him not to enjoy it. Ben Baker sulked off, and I went and joined Ben Fields and John Chomsky to play a game we invented.

The end of lunchtime dinner bell rang, and I headed back to Miss Harris' class. I entered through the patio door, a route that was frowned upon as it was meant as an emergency exit and usually would cost me a bollocking but that day I didn't care. Feeling a little low, and a little sweaty I sat in my usual seat and leaned my head back against the window, pensively looking out at the summer sun. I began to peer around the room watching other kids return from the playground slowly. A few moments later, after I had fully regained my focus and stopped daydreaming I noticed Ben Baker's Pog folder on the table two seats down. It was his entire collection of Pogs, special editions from America and a Kini collection all in one folder, the equivalent to Wikileaks finding the entire Area 51's Majestic 12 dossier just abandoned on their lap. Ben was missing, he had not retuned yet. Immediately my mind went to work crafting a sneaky plan to get back at him. It had to be sneaky but not too naughty. I couldn't steal the Pogs, that was straight up thievery and the reprisal bollocking for that, should I be caught, would be too much for me to handle. Instead, I quickly found a patsy.

"Anna," I called, to Anna Campbell who was sitting at the next table.

"What?" she asked.

"Would you like my Pog collection, I got a complete series 1, most of 2 and 3 as well as some rare blades and Tazos?" I replied.

"Don't you want them?" she asked back.

"Nah, bored of them now, but they're in skill condition, I'm just trying to get rid of them really," I said quickly, knowing Ben could pop his head around the corner any minute blundering the transaction.

"How much you want for them?" she enquired.

"Nothing, they're free! Do you want them or not!" I almost shouted out of impatience to secure the deal.

"Yeah, alright, thanks very much!" she said smiling. She must have thought I had a crush on her or something, unaware of the politics behind my benevolence. I handed them over swiftly and she laid them on the table in front of her examining them. I knew there was nothing I could do about this as it would come off too suspicious. I wanted to tell her to hide them away, to put them in her bag, anything, but I couldn't. Moments later, Ben came in with his entourage of mates including Adam Daniels, Dan Dyson and Dean Bronson. Immediately, he knew something was missing. He looked at the table, checked his bag, looked at me, I just shrugged my shoulders and said "What?" pretending to be clueless. His eyes scanned the room and quickly he located his Pog folder open at Anna Campbell's desk with her pawing through the collection.

"Shit," I sighed under my breath.

"Anna, why have you got my Pog folder?" he asked fairly patiently.

"Michael gave it to me, said it was his, said I could have it," Anna quickly replied.

"Oh did he now? Well, I'm sorry to say it's actually mine, and I'd like to have it back now, please," Ben said.

"Oh, sorry, misunderstanding I guess, so sorry Ben, here you go," she said softly enraptured by his blue eyes and handing him back the folder.

"It's not your fault." Ben smiled back at Anna charmingly (it was disgusting) then glared at me furiously. As he made his way back to his seat clasping his Pog folder like a life vest, he muttered "Pathetic" at me and petulantly kicked my table before sitting down. In fairness, it was pathetic and humiliating. At best, I had slightly inconvenienced him and in the process watched as he had charmed yet another girl in the class to his whim so easily. I laid my elbows and forearms on the table in front of me making a rectangle shape and sunk my head down into it. A couple of seconds later I felt a nudge from Steve McDougal who was sitting to my left.

"It's okay, Sleggs, I'd have done the same!" This level of compassion and solidarity for something so stupid shouldn't have made me feel better, but it did.

A couple hours of mandatory learning later and the end of the day bell rang. Before we left, we were all given permission slips to be signed by parents or guardian regarding a school trip to Hampton Court Palace. We had been studying the Tudors for the past term and had even learnt a catchy song about them (bits of which I can still remember to this day).

Unlike the majority of my days at St Paul's, on this occasion, I had arranged to stay behind for a couple of hours after school to use the computers with Steve. We fed the teacher the pretence of work-related nonsense, but in actuality, we were planning on playing Lemmings for the entire period before the janitors packed up and went home. Convinced by our alibi and impressed at our thirst for education (yeah, right), she gave us access to one computer. These were the days before internet, YouTube and Facebook, so there was really very little to exploit other than education from a school PC. Still if there was anything of non-academic amusement, you can be sure the students would sniff it out. The second the teacher was out of sight, we closed down the word document we had brought up as a guise, and loaded 'Lemmings' from a pirate floppy disc I had bought off Matthew Norris (a kid in the year above) at a garage sale, a few days prior, for 50p. Five minutes in Steve and I were having a whale of a time taking turns on alternate levels to rescue the Lemmings from their ill fates. We had been playing for about half an hour when all of a sudden, on level 16, it crashed.

At first, I tried clicking the mouse frantically, followed by the traditional CTRL ALT DELETE combo to close the game. Nothing. Steve and I looked at each other, feeding off each other's panic.

"What do we do?" he asked beginning to sweat.

"I don't know!" I nervously replied, the heat and prickles rising up my back to my neck.

"You know computers, don't you?" Steve begged.

"Only a little, besides all I got is a commodore 64, and I've never seen this before," I desperately reasoned, trying to absolve myself of any guilt.

"Think, logically Mike, what happens, when a game doesn't load on your commodore 64, what do you do?" Steve said clambering for some self-control.

"I dunno, it's never happened, I guess I'd turn the commodore off and on again and reload the tape and hope for the best, but that's the commodore, it could be a completely different ball park here," I quivered. Steve and I sat silent waiting for a miracle. Nothing. The screen had been locked on its original state for the past 5 minutes and an annoying buzzing tone was all that remained of the Lemmings soundtrack blasting through the speakers.

"Right, well we'll try that. We got nothing else to lose," Steve gulped. I took a big breath.

"On your head, be it mate," my shaky voice muttered as I pushed the on-off switch at the front of the PC. After a couple of uncertain seconds, the machine powered down and switched off.

"How long do we wait for?" I asked.

"I dunno, it's either 5 or 20 seconds," Steve answered.

"Which one? Does it have to be exact?" I quaked.

"I dunno, let's make it 20 to be sure though," Steve whined back.

We both held our collective breath for what seemed like an eternity, then once again pressed the on-off switch and waited. Nothing, the machine just sat there idly mocking us. Terrified I rapidly pushed the on-off switch a multitude of times, screaming, "Come on, ya bastard," and smacking the tower on the side desperately trying to revive it. Much like the kid on the railway in the movie 'Stand by me', the computer wasn't sick, the computer wasn't sleeping, the computer was dead.

"Shiiiiiiiit!" Steve and I cursed simultaneously, looking at each other, then grabbed our backpacks and legged it out of the school. We reached the junction where we both went our separate way home, both trying futilely to calm each other down and convince ourselves that it'll be magically fixed in the morning, and we'll both laugh about it in days to come. I'm sure at the time, we both realised this was not true, but the lies were good tonic to soothe our troubled minds, at least until the following day.

I barely got any sleep that night, and when the next morning arose, I tried to pull a sickie. 'Course my mum wasn't having any of it. She wouldn't let me stay home from school even if I was genuinely ill, unless I was on death's door and even then she and my dad would make damn sure I wouldn't have access to any entertainment such as TV. It had been a serious bone of contention for me growing up, especially when I heard of other friends staying off sick only to luxuriate with video games, unbridled TV access, movies and room service by their caring parents. My parents' excuse never changed. "If you're too sick to go to school, you're too sick to watch TV," they'd say, utter nonsense and we both knew it. To this day, they still have a lot to be held accountable for.

As I rode down to school that morning, dark clouds began to form, and it began to piss it down, an omen of things to come. I cautiously locked my bike up and began the long walk to class. I walked slowly hoping for a distraction to take me away. Hell, I would rather have been kidnapped than face the music that day. As I hesitantly entered the classroom, I spotted the row of computers sitting there, all on, all working. I couldn't believe my luck, I glanced over at Steve who was beaming at me, we mouthed a couple of 'What the …?',and 'I know right!' statements to each other across the void, but tried to remain subtle in case we roused any suspicion. I walked in confidently, sighing with relief and took my place next to Steve, both of us were giggling quietly now with relief. Miss Harris began talking.

"Right class, today we're gonna learn about Catherine of Aragon. I'll hand out some worksheets, and in a few minutes, there'll be a quiz on them," Miss Harris said kindly. Steve and I were still of good cheer as I remarked,

"Silly, what were we worried about, I knew this'd blow over, didn't I say?"

"Yeah," Steve replied taking a worksheet and passing the pile on.

"Michael Sleggs, Steve McDougal, can I have a word!?" Harris continued. Steve and I both looked back in terror. We had not escaped death's clutches after all, and we both immediately knew it as we noticed the tone in Harris' voice drop and all the love leave her face.

Immediately, the prickles and heat began to storm their way back up my spine and neck, and I started to sweat profusely.

"I thought you wanted us to get on with the sheet?" I stuttered, hoping to buy some time, an alternative, anything!

"Come here now," Harris commanded, sterner than ever beckoning with her index finger. I was almost sick from worry as both Steve and I walked up to her desk. She got up and took us into the next room by the computers.

"Right boys, what happened last night!?" Harris screeched.

"What do you mean?" we both answered quickly, too in sync with each other. It was suspicious.

"When I arrived this morning, we had to call a special technician to fix the computer, it took 2 hours and cost £500," she barked.

"Why, what happened to it?" I said, clinging desperately to my oblivious mask, though it was too late, my eyes told her everything and Steve was glancing down at the ground just to avoid any give away. A wise move I thought.

"You know full well, you did something to it last night. Something that broke it, what did you do?" she boomed back at us.

"You mean all my saved work is lost, ah no, I worked for hours on the research for my Tudor project, even read through pages on Encarta '94 to make sure I had my bases covered. Made 15 pages of notes on the subject in word too," I feebly retorted, still foolishly clawing to a pathetic backstory I was making up as I was going along. Even Steve was sighing by now, probably mostly from embarrassment, he nudged me slightly giving me that look that says, 'you gotta learn when to quit and take your hits'. See for him, trouble had followed him around his entire life. He was constantly in trouble for this or that, and while he didn't like it anymore that I did, he had learnt vital lessons on doing the dance, which I had not. In fairness, this was admirable, and I was looking more pathetic by the minute.

"So you're saying, everything was working fine when you left?" Harris said. It seemed for a moment, that she had conceded and I had pulled a rabbit out of the hat, threaded the eye of the needle and regardless of my guilt-stricken face, my acting and story had done its job.

"Yeah… I mean yes, Miss Harris," I coughed. The room stank of farts by this point due to the high stress levels both mine and Steve's little 8-year-old bodies had been under. Our bowels were just not biologically trained to cope with such an event. If this were a smell test, we would have been caught out in the first minute. Miss Harris, leaned her giant curly haired head back thinking for a while, although this was all part of her act. Turns out she was a massive fan of detective shows and had an ace up her sleeve.

"Okay, you boys can go," she said, softly. The tension left my shoulders like a massive weight, whatever happened I would need a serious sports massage later, but that, as it turns out would be the least of my worries. As we turned and began to walk our way back to the main classroom, we were only a few feet away from the door, still unsure of how we convinced her of our innocence. We crept slowly like two children trapped in a tiger cage edging towards the exit.

"Oh there was just one more thing," Harris continued. We stopped like statues then slowly looked back to face Harris.

"The technician recovered this from the computer," Harris said, walking towards both of us placing the Lemmings floppy disc in my hand. It had been branded with a stamp that read 'Property of Michael Sleggs', just so there was no confusion. A stamp I had gotten as a Christmas gift earlier that year, a gift that I hated but had tried to make the most of, a stamp that would seal my fate that day. Man, I hated that stamp. Harris immediately grabbed both of us by our collars.

"Did you really think you could just walk away from this?" she whispered in our ears like some terrifying European bad guy in an 80s action movie. I could feel her hot breath as it sank its way deep into my cochlea, finally, condensating to moisture and feeling like a tickly wet-willy. Moments later, she was frog marching us up to Mrs Butterworth's office. As Steve and I were pushed and shoved and manhandled towards the office, much like lemmings, we were on a hopeless trajectory towards death. I pictured two coffins being prepared by the undertaker and two tombstones standing in the conservation area of the school. That was after a public execution of both of us on the school field. It was all so real and all so scary. To this day I've blocked out the bulk of those old school bollockings, but suffice to say my fearful daydreams paint an accurate metaphorical image of the events of that day. I still dream about them sometimes, and every time I do, another hair turns grey on my head like an eternal curse that will follow me till the end of my days.

Chapter 7
The Trials of Hampton Court

It was cold, wet and raining the day we all lined up in disjointed single file to climb aboard the National Express bus bound for Hampton Court Palace. We had been studying the Tudors all term, and this was the final hurrah before the summer break. It was meant as a learning experience, but to us students who had no interest in academia it was a welcome respite from the ball and chain of the classroom. I suppose in some ways the teachers saw it as a day off too, as the tour guides would do all the teaching once inside the palace and their roles of 'teacher' would be relegated to 'glorified baby sitter'.

It was roughly 8:17 am when I stepped onto the bus that morning making my way up the aisle and perching next to Steve McDougal somewhere midway on the right. At the back of the bus, Steve's brother Patrick sat next to his best friend, Andrew Murphy. Theirs was a friendship that, like a shooting star, burned intense but also burned brief. See, Andrew had eyes for Patrick's girlfriend at the time, Xenia Brand (who wouldn't?), and by the end of the trip, he would be seen smooching her at the back of the bus. As with a lion taking over a pride, the lesser man (Patrick) would be evicted from the pride and his pride was shattered. Side note, I cleverly used both meanings of the word pride there, which I realise will likely be wasted on the incompetent and slow of brain, but I trust you get the point. Also, since we're on the subject of lions, I feel I may as well mention an interesting fact that may add credence to this whole affair. Lions have 5x better eyesight than humans' eyes, so if Xenia was fit to human eyes, one can only imagine how hot she was to Andrew. In fairness, no one could blame him for sticking a knife is his best friends back in that scenario.

Molly Harper was the last in line to board the bus and once she sat down next to her ginger best friend Molly Anderson, we all waited patiently for the bus to depart. Five minutes passed. Nothing. We weren't moving. There was a bit of commotion between the teachers at the front of the bus, which eventually died down. Occasionally, Mrs Rudley would look at her watch, tut, and then sprint out of the bus to Mrs Butterworth's office and back again. What was going on? What was the hold up? 15 minutes passed. Nothing. 30 minutes passed. Still nothing. The bus stood stationary. By this point, even the students on the bus were starting to revolt from boredom, although clueless about the situation, we had all ran out of our best chat and were getting impatient, some weaker willed ones complaining they needed to pee. Eventually, 46 minutes later, a car screeched to a halt on the opposite side of the road. It was a rusty old looking, trash-filled station wagon. A small, quiet, "oh crap!" left my lips, when I peered out of the grubby window upon seeing this car. Next a fat sow looking boy and his half-cut mother opened the doors of the car and exited, running frantically towards the bus. Rudley stood outside looking pissed. The two women had a brief heated exchange and Kevin was practically thrown on to the bus tripping over his untied shoelaces as he entered. Pam blew a kiss and waved to Kevin who was being manhandled into the seat by Rudley in a swift, impatient manner.

"Let's go!" Rudley shouted with fury as the bus driver started the engine and departed at 9:09 am, a whole 39 minutes behind schedule. As the bus pulled away and Pam was left in the dust, Kevin, who barely noticed the irritated look on everyone's face, got to work immediately picking his nose. Occasionally, he'd glance up at Rudley sitting next to him, finger still in nose, and she would look back contemptuously and emit an angry grunt.

About half an hour into the bus ride, Steve and I were in strong chat about video game giants Sega and Nintendo and who had the better games. Similar chats about movies, Pogs and Snakeboards filled the mouths of the other seated pairs of children within the bus. The lesser kids who had no chat relied on their Walkman as a crutch offering the second earpiece to their partner as a goodwill gesture, as if to make amends for their boring personality. Unfortunately, due to the medium of tape at the time, the music choice was somewhat limited and repetitive. On a different school trip, to Wookey Hole Caves, one year I listened to 'I'll be there for you' by The Rembrandts 292 times on repeat whilst sitting next to Ben Rickets because he had nothing to say for himself. By the end of it, I felt like one of those detainees at Guantanamo Bay, who get sensory deprivation torture save for a screaming sound coming from earphones. Ben Rickets was and still is easily the most boring man I have ever met, and that was easily the longest, most mind-numbing journey of my life. Needless to say, I won't be there for him.

We pulled into the bus park around 11 am, the bus driver had made reasonably good time considering it was a two-hour journey, but we were still a good half hour behind our intended ETA. Mrs Harris and another teacher, Mr Oaken, exited first. Rudley stood up and made some generic announcement about pairing up and waiting outside the bus for further instructions once everyone had departed. She then took Kevin forcefully by the hand, and dragged him off the bus. Kevin tried fruitlessly to engage in a brief conversation with the disinterested and tired looking bus driver about the engine size of such a vehicle, but neither Rudley nor the bus driver would give him the time of day as he was slowing down the line.

"Shut up!" Rudley snapped at Kevin, and she heaved his heavy stout body away from the bus driver and down the steps to the side of the bus like a prison commandant. Steve and I chuckled with laughter as we made our way down the gangway and watched Kevin getting told off behind the glass window of the bus, like a silent pantomime. Eventually, we had all exited the bus and stood nearby in our pairs chatting amongst ourselves. Rudley had one final brief word with the bus driver who looked exhausted and had heavy sweat patches seeping through his white polyester shirt. The bus driver drove away to park up and presumably rest, or maybe wither and die. It was hard to tell at this point from the look of him. Rudley, contained her dishevelled composure and marched back to the group. She glanced at the group hurriedly with her eyes scanning the numbers. The amount was correct, we hadn't lost any kids during the drive. This was good news, but, as she continued to gaze like a hawk along the pairs, her eyes turned steely. Everyone was paired up, everyone but Kevin. He was the odd man out.

"Michael!" Rudley shrieked like a banshee, "You pair up with Kevin, I'll take Steve!"

"Ahhh, what!?" I whined and slowly slumped my way over to Kevin's side. A sardonic smile crossed Rudley's face for a moment. She had had it in for me since I joined St Paul's, and I still didn't know why. Maybe my sister had pissed her off in earlier days, and she had cruelly decided that the sins of the sister shall be visited upon the brother or had adopted the 3-generation punishment fashioned by the North Korean Dictator Kim Jung-Un. Who knows? Either way it was terribly unfair.

As I made my way over to Kevin, the first observation I made was that he, unlike every other student that day, was wearing his school uniform. Now, the teachers had clearly stated in the permission slip that since this was an out of school trip, we were permitted to wear non-school uniform. They had granted us this luxury under the pretence of making it feel less of a work trip to us and more fun. But the real reason behind it I believe was in the off chance of kids misbehaving the teachers could have plausible deniability in ownership of the child until it was time again to leave. With no uniform came no link tying the school's good name to the naughty kid. MI5 employ a similar scheme of disavowing all knowledge of their agents, their missions and their involvement should they be caught or captured during their assignment. It was a clever tactic I'll give them that, but like most things left to chance, it would be foiled by some unexpected, stupid anomaly, which they hadn't accounted for in their planning. In this case, Kevin Blankenhorn was that stupid anomaly.

The day pressed on and by about 12 pm our tour was well underway. We had been shown around the reception and dropped facts (which I've since forgotten) by the tour guide about the different paintings adorning the walls of the hallway and made our way to Henry the VIII's bedchamber. A red rope was hung on small pylons which divided the space between us tourists and the bed. It was a subtle warning that this was a look but don't touch tour. The tour guide began telling us about the chamber pots, which while it grossed out a lot of us, one kid found funny. So funny, in fact, that his foul cackle echoed in the unnecessarily large room. It was Kevin's laugh. Except, Kevin was missing. Where was he? Immediately, Rudley looked at my side where

Kevin should have been, then glared at me like I was his keeper. It was difficult for the brief moment to identify the location of the laugh due to the immense echo, but just like that, as quickly as it started, it stopped. Silence fell upon the room. Rudley looked Trunchbullesque sniffing the air for a scent of Wotsits dust.

"Booo!" Kevin boomed, jumping out from under the covers followed by a filthy cascade of chuckling.

"That does it!" screamed Rudley who swiftly marched over to Kevin, vaulting the red rope divider like an Olympian and pushing the tour guide to her ass in the process. Rudley seized Kevin's arm and dragged him out like the Terminator as he clung desperately to the bed sheets subsequently pulling them off the bed. Quickly, Rudley apologised to the tour guide and took Kevin to the corner of the room and gave him a massive telling off. Her long windy fingers were practically jabbing his face as her rage desperately demanded an outlet. I assume he was taken to the corner of the room to be discreet, but we could hear and see everything. Steve jumbled his way through the crowd next to me to grab front row seats as it were. All the boys were sniggering to themselves including me and Steve and all the girls were just aghast with shock. Then we all witnessed one of the most wonderful things I think we collectively got to see. Around the three-minute mark of scolding and poking, something inside Kevin snapped and he slapped Rudley in the face. Steve and I looked at each other and back at the situation with the most excited anticipation ever to be seen upon a child's face. For a moment, Rudley seemed as shocked as we were, but within a microsecond, she recharged like Pikachu does before his electric attack and bellowed the largest seemingly relentless tirade of bitter, exasperated indignation any of us had ever seen. Kevin's hair was literally blowing in the wind of her breath and his flabby chungs reverberating like the characters in a Dolby surround sound cinema adverts. I don't think to this day, I or any of my classmates have beheld anything quite so glorious in our lives.

Twenty minutes later, we had made our way to the grounds and were perusing the gardens and workers' smaller residences. The journey from the palace to the grounds wasn't far, so everyone walked, everyone but me. I had seen the odd horse drawn carriage milling around the place and decided now was the perfect time to milk my congenital heart disease card. I scurried towards Miss Rudley who was leading our gaggle down the path. Acting puffed out I exclaimed I couldn't go any further without a break.

"We can't well stop the tour, Michael! We're running late as it is," Rudley brutally rebuffed. She had fallen right into my trap.

"Well, if I die on a school trip due to too much of an erratic heart beat…" I paused, watching the concern flood Rudley's face.

"'Course, there are many of these carriages pottering about, perhaps you could ask if they could give me a lift to the workers' cottage," I slyly petitioned. Rudley's head sunk, then she slowed down and explained the situation to Mr Oaken who was a few feet behind. Mr Oaken then grabbed the attention of the class and informed them that he was now the leader. Meanwhile, Rudley, rudely snapped her fingers, pointed and shouted. "You!" to one of the nearby carriages. The driver, dressed in full top hat and tails, although startled, took the prompting very well and remained in pomp character whilst slowing the carriage down to a halt.

"Yes, me lady?" he replied.

"We have a sick child here, we need to get to the cottages, we're climbing aboard, and don't call me lady," Rudley snapped as she and I climbed on board at the back seats. The driver, who must have been used to being treated as an under servant, brushed off Rudley's rude orders rather well. The fact that she didn't even ask, or say please astonished me. He simply said, "Right," then cracked his reins as we rode off towards the cottage. Meanwhile, through the dust I could see my peers looking on with jealousy and hear their whining in the wind. It was a beautiful moment, and I made the most of it by waving at my tired comrades à la Macaulay Culkin in Home Alone as the wet bandits are driven off by the police. My face reeked of smugness. Of course I wasn't sick. Of course I wouldn't have died. Granted I did have congenital heart defects but nothing that would have prevented me from walking the distance. I saw this as my first foray into 'opportunism', and to this day, I'm still proud of my charade.

As the day continued, we were introduced to Hampton Court's illustrious Shining like hedge maze. We were all handed maps and told to meet at the exit in an hour. Once again, we were all paired up, and I was forced to draw the short straw and be coupled with Kevin. Even though the maze was moderately vast, the aid of a map made navigation child's play. Unfortunately, despite my best efforts of convincing him that the quickest way to complete it was to take a brief moment before embarking to mark out our route on the map and then follow it, Kevin obstinately snatched the map out of my hand and ran into the maze shouting, "Come on, we gotta win."

Frantically, I looked back at Rudley with my best 'this isn't fair' face, at which point, she replied with the same smug look I had played in the carriage and even waved bye to match. As I chased into the maze hunting Kevin's heavy-set footsteps, I heard her yell, "You boys better make it to the exit quick, it'll be dark soon."

Five minutes later, I turned a corner to find Kevin fastening his trouser button.

"What's going on?" I asked.

"Dead end," Kevin sniffed.

"I can see that Kevin! Where's the map?" I angrily rebuffed!

"Chucked it, it was slowing us down," Kevin stubbornly answered.

"What!? How!?" I said furiously.

"Don't worry, I have a secret weapon," he said with a proud grin on his stupid looking face. Kevin reached into his cheap grey polyester school trouser pocket and pulled something out. Brushing aside the pile of lint and pencil sharpenings that surrounded the item he showed me his 'secret weapon'. Upon his grey, pig-like hand sat a Tony the tiger compass. This was quite possibly the very thing that made him late that morning as he incompletely manhandled his way through his box of Frosties (more than likely tearing the box and crushing the cereal in the process) to retrieve it.

"Great okay, so you know which direction the exit is then, right?" I keenly asked, clearly knowing that a map was more useful but trying to cut Kevin some slack.

"Well, I think it might be North," Kevin replied.

"Think? Might?" I snapped again realising we were as good as lost. "What makes you think that then, Kevin?"

"Uh, a hunch," he stuttered, his chin wobbling as he struggled to find a better reason. "Besides, little known fact, a compass is never wrong?" he continued confidently puffing his chest out like he had cracked the code, answered the question correctly and as if he was privy to some insider information.

"Yes Kevin, but that fact becomes irrelevant if we don't know which direction the exit is!" I yelled, absolutely livid by this point.

"No, no, no…'cuz…" Kevin replied. I could almost see the hamster running its last breath around the wheel inside Kevin's brain as, exhausted, his thinking came to a stop.

"Umm…" Kevin murmured, scratching his head, then sniffing his fingers, completely oblivious to the avalanche of dandruff that came with the motion.

"Right, I'm outta here!" I said flatly, ditching Kevin and bounding around the corner quickly to look for another pair with more sense.

"You won't get anywhere without me and my compass!" Kevin shouted back, his voice growing fainter as the distance between us increased.

Twenty minutes and five different routes later, I was reaching the end of my tether.

"Argh, I'm gonna die in this stupid maze!" I screamed, looking up at the dying light of day through the limited view of the hedge path. Suddenly, I heard footsteps and talking coming from the other side of the hedge.

"Hello!" I called. The footsteps stopped. Through the tiny breaks in the branches I saw the silhouette of two kids.

"Michael?" a voice called back.

"Andrew?" I replied.

"Michael, what are you doing there?" he chuckled.

"I'm lost, aren't I?" I replied in a disgruntled manner.

"What? Why? What happened to your map?" Andrew asked.

"Kevin!" I answered crossly, saying his name through gritted teeth as if it were a cuss word.

"Ah, say no more. Well, we're real close to the exit, if you like, we'll come back for you." Andrew sympathetically offered.

"Ah, really? That would be great, thank you so much," I gratefully responded.

"Right, looking at the map I think I can figure out where you're at, but just in case let's be smart about this," Andrew remarked from the other side of the hedge. For a moment, I stood puzzled by what he meant till he broke the silence once again calling out a loud audible, "Marco!"

"Polo," I responded and thought to myself, sometimes the simplest things are the most genius, except Kevin, he was simple without merit.

"Marco."

"Polo."

"Marco."

"Polo."

Within five minutes, I began to hear two sets of footsteps heading my way and then from around the corner, Andrew's head poked out with a happy smile adorned on his face!

"Peekaboo," he joked as he spotted me. I chuckled and beamed back. Ten minutes later, under the guidance of Andrew, his silent partner Xenia and their map all three of us had made it out of the maze. We were still 10 minutes ahead of schedule as we made our way to the bus. Several other children were already standing nearby, whilst some slower, dumber stragglers were still coming out of the maze in the distance, the look of relief washing over their little faces as they saw us in our line up against the bus. Pretty soon afterwards Rudley began her register. Everyone was present and accounted for, save for one name. Kevin Blankenhorn. Rudley continued through the register to see if there was any other lost souls, but alas, only the one stuck out like a sore thumb. Quickly, she switched the papers in her hand to a list of the pairs she had established at the beginning of the day.

Murmuring furiously to herself I could only watch as her crone like finger made its way down the list to Kevin's name and next to it was mine. I saw her mouth the words Michael Sleggs, as if in slow motion. Next, she did a double take as she saw I was present and accounted for before concocting her scapegoat bollocking.

"Michael, I'm only gonna ask this once, where is Kevin?"

"I don't know, Miss Rudley, somewhere in there, lost," I replied with a carefree attitude. I had had enough of babysitting that brat and having to take shit for the sake of it.

"Where in there?" she repeated angrily. I folded my arms in defiance then gestured loosely towards the maze.

"How should I know, it's a maze, innit!" I sarcastically replied, I was in no mood for games.

"Well, where did you last see him?" she was getting desperate, her bravado of confidence in being able to pin the blame on me slipping.

"I dunno, somewhere near the beginning? I thought you were only gonna ask me this question once, that's three times now," I cockily remarked. Rudley stormed towards me pinning me to the side of the bus with her body. Exhaling fiercely out of her nostrils like a bull she boomed:

"Why did you leave him, you stupid boy!?!"

"He threw away the map, we had no chance, and he was slowing me down with his obstinance. Whatever happens is on you," I boldly retorted. To this day, I can't believe I had the balls to say it, true as it may have been. Rudley's reserve confidence crumpled like a sack of shit as she frantically began looking in different directions as if to find some answer. She knew she would be held responsible when the chips came down.

A half hour went by, and the dusk was beginning to set in. By this point, all of us students had made our way onto the bus and were chatting about the day and laughing about the maze dilemma amongst ourselves. Outside, Rudley stood vigilant coming back inside on occasion to make the odd phone call via the bus phone to the Hampton Court authorities trying to organise a search and rescue party. Time was ticking on, and we were already past due at home. An hour had passed and the rescue was underway. The Hampton Court team understood the time sensitive conditions of this operation so they reluctantly agreed to the use of a helicopter and ground team. The helicopter would locate Kevin and hover above, whilst the ground team would make their way towards the location. Twenty minutes later, Kevin was found waving a branch with his under pants threaded through in some sort of make shift flag. Aggressively, they took him and frog marched him back to the bus. It was 8:07 pm by the time they reached the bus and made the hand over to Rudley. Sternly the rescue party leader made it known to Rudley that the Hampton Court Palace will be sending a bill in the post to St Paul's school to pay for the rescue op and advised her in future to keep a closer eye on her flock. You could literally see the steam rise from Rudley's frazzled head as she took the bollocking. Meanwhile, Kevin was interrupting the whole time saying proudly, "They found me 'cuz I cleverly used my underwear as a flag on the end of a stick. That's the good thing about being in a hedge, lots of sticks to use!"

He kept shoving his skid marked underwear on the stick in and around Rudley's face in an attempt to illicit some praise for his 'clever thinking'.

"Kevin, shut up and sit down!" Rudley exploded. Kevin stood dumbfounded. Then Rudley wrestled him to his seat. In the ruckus, she paused for a moment, sniffing the air like a bloodhound. There was a faint waft of shit coming from inside Kevin's backpack. Aggressively, Rudley yanked it off Kevin and unzipped it. She pulled out a clear Tupperware lunch box. Gingerly, she began to open it to discover a turd and a piece of paper.

"What is the meaning of this!?" she spoke, her face as red as a tomato with rage.

"I needed the loo," he replied very matter-a-factly.

"And this, the map?" Rudley breathed quietly between her teeth.

"I needed to wipe myself with something," Kevin responded, again proud of his ingenious idea, thinking he was a regular Bear Grylls. Most of the boys on the bus just chuckled, but the wussier ones joined the girls in a united gasp.

Rudley lost it. Immediately she put the lid back on and threw the entire Tupperware box out of the window!

"DRIVE!" she shrieked at the bus driver who was up to this point laughing with the rest of the boys on the bus.

Rudley sat in silence next to Kevin the entire journey back. The rest of us went about our usual conversations. Tired and ready for bed, we arrived back at the school at 9:30 pm. There were police cars as well as many angry looking parents nearby who had no clue where their kids had been for the past 3 hours. A lonely, bored looking lollipop man sat on the St Paul's school wall awaiting his time to shine. The doors of the bus flung open and a ragged Miss Rudley practically fell out into a wall of hateful abuse and finger pointing by frustrated parents. Mr Oaken tried his best to take command and ease the parents' annoyance but to little avail. Slowly the kids filed out of the bus, reuniting with their parents and the commotion eventually died down. Ironically, because of the three-hour delay getting back, my mum arrived nearly on time for once, sauntering in at a respectable 9:35 pm. She had no knowledge of our three-hour delay, so this was just when she intended to pick me up regardless. To this day I still look back fondly on that trip to Hampton Court Palace, despite its cockups. The memory of Kevin getting told off, Rudley getting slapped, my smug attitude on the horse drawn carriage, my strength of character and backbone for not taking any more of Rudley's unfair shit, and the odd bonds you make with friends throughout the day still warm the cockles of my heart. However, to this day, I can't remember a single academic thing learnt from that trip.

Chapter 8
The Impalement of Dan Kent

A new school year had begun at St Paul's and as usual our class had gone through some changes. Some innocuous, some less so. Everyone had returned from their summer break, and were catching up on the trivial gossip that surrounds such things. Ben Baker was showing off the fact that he had spent his holidays in Florida at Disneyland; meanwhile, Kevin was showing off his fungal foot infection that absolutely stank to high heaven. Richard Slate had had his appendix removed and was playing it up like a near death experience. Sam Barnsley's voice had dropped, and he was already beginning to shave; he was nine years old for crying out loud! Meanwhile, the biggest news I had was about getting a snakeboard for my birthday.

As we all calmed down, registration began and a tall, lanky, ginger kid popped down next to me and quietly unzipped his pencil case pulling out a pencil and a protractor and placing them in an anally retentive fashion in front of him making a right angle on the table. I looked at him, puzzled and a little put out by the new face that had now unwarrantedly joined our table. He hadn't asked, he hadn't been invited. There were still plenty of other free seats at other tables he could have plopped down on. I continued to stare at him, my glare getting more and more toxic by the second, and he continued to ignore me. Not only did this kid have the audacity of sitting at the cool kids' table uninvited, but also he didn't even have the good grace to introduce himself. Eventually, the ginger youngling glanced my way, and I motioned the 'what gave?' body language. I even mixed in a bit of extra scorn to hopefully drill home how rude and presumptuous his actions had been. He looked at me and scoffed in a condescending manner then continued to stare straight ahead. Mr Smith (a substitute teacher we had for approximately one day) started reading out the register.

"Ben Adams."

"Yep."

"Sam Barnsley."

"Here."

"Ben Baker."

"Yep."

"Adam Blackburn."

"Yeah."

"Alex Carter."

"Yeah."

"John Chomsky."

"Yeah."

"Adam Daniels."

"Yep."

"Dan Kent."

"Yes, Mr Smith," whispered the ginger kid shyly.

"Dan Kent," he repeated.

"Here," he said, lifting his quivering right hand in the air to identify himself.

What a pussy, I thought, and my look of annoyance slowly morphed into a disgusted grimace as I looked down at the table shaking my head. The shaking of my head stopped on a dime a few seconds later, and my eyes opened wide as I realised I recognised that name. I started racking my brain, where had I heard it before? I was so wrapped up in thinking that when Mr Smith called my name out, I was completely oblivious. It wasn't until the third, "Michael Sleggs," that I snapped out of it and replied with the ever cool, "Here, unfortunately," a joke I used very often, but always got a laugh.

Nowadays, I'd admonish myself for the overuse of the same joke, but when you're a kid, you can laugh for days at something you consider witty even when it's repeated at nauseam. Finally it clicked, Dan Kent, I knew that name from a skip rope rhyme I had heard the girls singing during break time and lunches.

He's gay.
He's bent.
His arse is up for rent.
Dan Kent.
Dan Kent.

The song had been made up by some anonymous genius, a couple years above us and since it dropped had spread like wild fire among the years. If this had been 2012, it would be auto tuned in a YouTube video.

"So you're Dan Kent?" I laughed.

"Yes," he coyly replied.

"The Dan Kent from the infamous skip rope rhyme?" I said with a twisted smile on my face.

"The very same," he said, with a proud smile on his face. It was weird, I couldn't for the life of me understand why this kid was proud of a song that mocked him, as if it was some kind of achievement or something.

As the day progressed, Steve and I grew more and more irritated with Dan's pestilence. It wasn't so much that he did much, just that he was there, and his presence, no matter how banal, had a severely damaging impact on the table's cool factor. In other words, our stock was plummeting, and school as everyone knows is one big popularity contest, the rest is just background noise.

Lunchtime arrived, and Steve and I were glad to get out and make as much distance from Dan as possible to show that our association ended outside the classroom and was not a deliberate choice. Sadly, as good as our intentions were, we had not banked on the biology of the situation. For every 10 steps we took, Dan—with the freakishly long legs for his age—needed only one. Steve and I tried our best to out run him sprinting like gazelles among the St Paul's school field but, no matter what, he kept pace with just a few small strides. Eventually, tired from the chase, we couldn't go any further and collapsed like a heap on the floor.

"What are you doing, Dan?" I puffed.

"Wanna play a game?" he enquired.

"No, hence the running," I angrily retorted still catching my breath.

"I thought we were playing tag?" Dan petitioned, his lanky shadow looming over the two of us.

"No, you didn't," Steve said gruffly.

"Oh, okay. Well, I have one more question," Dan replied.

"Oh, what?" I groaned impatiently.

"Do you reckon the girls in the school all fancy me?" he asked, in a disconcertingly genuine tone.

"What? No not at all, what a stupid thing to say," I answered with a chortle.

"I reckon they do, if they didn't, they wouldn't sing that jump rope song," he replied confidently.

"What!? How does that make any sense?" Steve came back.

"It's a well-known fact that women always tease the ones they fancy, but then again, maybe you're too immature to understand these more adult things," Dan responded, pulling back his sleeves and flexing his pale, white, pasty, thin, weedy freckle covered arms.

"Dan, when a girl gently teases you, yes it can be a sign of flirtation, but when someone goes to the effort of writing a poem specifically intended to emasculate you and butcher your credibility as a straight man, it's not flirtation, it's repulsion," I responded annoyed at the arrogance of this ginger dweeb.

Steve continued, "The fact that all the other girls in the school have adopted this poem into their vernacular to skip rope to is merely a sign that that disgust is a shared consensus."

"Oh, well, I think you're wrong," Dan huffed and marched his way to the monkey bars only to get entangled upside down by his own lanky physique in the process of trying to show off to a few of the nearby onlookers. Eventually, his twisted body fell to the floor with a thud, and he brushed off the bark from his trousers then went and sat on the climbing frame till the end of lunch.

That afternoon, we were all busy doing an art project which basically consisted of drawing a Roman soldier, labelling his attire and colouring in the final picture. It was trivial but that's what education is at a primary school level sometimes. On the table, we only had a limited amount of stationery to share between Steve, Ben, Adam, myself, and now the latest addition Dan Kent. It was quite obvious we had barely got by with what we had with our original table population, and having another person punting for our rations was more than taking the piss. Between the original four of us, we had worked out a finally tuned system, which prevented squabbles and optimised our individual usage of each utensil. This system was soon thrown into disarray as Dan kept snatching whatever stationery he needed when he desired, without even asking. At first, this was a mere annoyance, but soon it turned impossible as he began snatching crayons out of the hands of others whilst they were using them. This became a bit too frustrating for Steve who was in the middle of colouring in a tunic, when Dan reached over and wrestled the crayon out of Steve's hand and in the process drew a nasty green line across Steve's page. Now, you have to admit, that would bring anyone's piss to a boil, especially when you've been so diligent to stay within the lines of the drawing. Steve lost it. A few seconds passed and Dan was busy colouring in his drawing with the stolen green crayon. His left hand sat idle on the desk next to his drawing. Quickly, Steve grabbed a number 2 HB pencil (one of the standard black and yellow striped Staedtler ones) from his Pepsi cola can shaped pencil case, took his sharpener and made it as sharp as an arrow. Steve then violently reached over and stabbed Dan through the left hand, sticking him to the table like some kind of makeshift classroom desk crucifixion.

An unquenchable orgasm of pain shrieked out of Dan's mouth, and the whole class fell silent and stared at the source. Steve stood by, licking his lips with satisfaction at his vengeance.

"Holy shit dude," I gasped, gob smacked, turning my gaze to Dan's hand and back to Steve's on looking face. Another wail followed as Dan grabbed the end of the pencil and unhinged himself from the table. Throwing the retracted stake from his hand he clutched his left palm trying hard to stop the bleeding. At this point, there was a lot of blood. Mr Smith sprinted over to Steve and grabbed him by the scruff of the neck. This was the closest I have ever seen a teacher being violent towards a student, though I'm sure it's more prominent than I would like to believe. Seizing him tightly Mr Smith boomed at Steve.

"Are you crazy, he could get lead poisoning, you complete idiot."

"Well, no 'cuz pencils contain graphite not lead," Steve answered back.

73

Mr Smith shook him intensely.

"If I have my way, you will be expelled, young man. What you have just done is totally unacceptable, and you should be ashamed yourself, you disgusting boy!" Mr Smith continued furiously. At this point, Steve's eyes were beginning to water. Mr Smith took a moment of heavy breathing and realised that the students were now all staring at him in slight disbelief and fear. Obviously, Steve had taken it too far, but instead of tending to Dan, Mr Smith was quite dominantly bullying Steve. It felt like that scene in Breakfast Club where Mr Vernon had John Bender in the supply closet and was threatening him. Eventually, Mr Smith loosened his grip and took Dan to the school nurse. I could see Steve was desperately trying to hold back the tears. I know he wasn't really the victim in this scenario either, but I can imagine the teacher's reaction gave him quite a scare.

"You alright, mate?" I cautiously asked, placing my hand on his shoulder. Steve took a breath then gulped, staring at all the blood. In truth, I don't think Steve meant to go that far, but he just saw red and snapped. Eventually, he calmed down, shook himself out of the shock and turned towards me.

"Yeah fine, mate, I think Mr Smith's bad breath made my eyes water," he joked wiping away the moisture that had accumulated in his eyes.

"It's fine pal, just take a moment and have a seat," I said gently.

"You first," he replied motioning down with his eyes causing me to look down. At this point, he made a circle between his thumb and index finger below the waist.

"Bastard." I laughed.

Steve chuckled and thumped me on the arm as was protocol for falling for the old, ring-shaped hand gesture.

"Impaling Dan wasn't enough, aye?" I asked shaking my head with a grin on my face.

"Oh yeah, it was, just felt like the right thing to do?" Steve responded shrugging his shoulders in a humorous manner. We both laughed and went about finishing our drawings. That day, Dan was removed out of our class permanently for his own safety, and Steve was given a two-week suspension from school. The time was quickly served, and Steve managed to stay out of major trouble for the rest of the years of our primary school education. A few months later, I found out it was, in fact, my sister who created the Dan Kent rhyme, and I was filled with pride, as I imagine she was in the knowledge that it became such a playground classic amongst her peers. In recent years, I've been in talks with her about releasing a single that expands on the Dan Kent Lament, but sadly as she's aged, she's lost the vision and isn't interested. It will exist now and forever as merely the song of that generation, and in fairness, there's a quiet dignity when the artist's creations are left unmolested. After all, remakes rarely surpass the original.

Chapter 9
The Most Embarrassing
Day of My Life

It was 8:03 am, on Monday the 26th of September 1994. I only remember the day because, well, to be honest, you don't forget a day like this. Autumn had set its weather in early, and the wind was howling outside my bedroom window.

"Michael, time to get up!" I heard my mum yell from the bottom of the stairs.

"Yeah, yeah!" I replied assuredly, then rolled over to a more comfortable position in my bed. I closed my eyes for a second, just to rest them, no intention of actually falling back to sleep again.

"MICHAEL! GET UP NOW!" my mum screamed furiously. I woke up with a startle and caught my breath. She had scared the hell out of me. Glancing at my clock I noticed time had just jumped forward 30 minutes. It was at that point that I realised one does not simply 'rest one's eyes' in the morning, and doing so can be a dangerous game.

I leapt out of bed. It was freezing which did nothing to lighten my mood from the rude awakening. A moment later, I gathered my polo shirt and St Paul's School jumper from the heap on the floor where I left it the night before and put them on. Next I found my trousers, picked them up and walked towards my sock drawer to find some underpants. Clawing through the mess one handed like a cat in a litter tray I was eventually forced to drop my trousers to conduct a proper, two-handed search. Within a minute, I had sorted through the entirety of my sock and underwear drawer and come up with nothing.

"Mum! Where are my pants?" I yelled in an impatient tone.

"In the wash still, they haven't been done yet," she shrieked back, this time from the landing.

"In the wash?" I said to myself in disbelief resting my head on the side of the chest of drawers.

"Well, what am I supposed to wear?" I called back.

"Here," she barged through the door.

"Just put these on, no one will know what you're wearing under your trousers," she said, throwing a pair of silk, pink, frilly panties that belonged to my sister my way.

"I'm not wearing them!" I angrily retorted.

"You don't have a choice! Put them on now, we're running late!" my mum boomed back. I knew I wasn't going to win this battle.

"Oh," I fussed slowly climbing into the panties that were far too big for me. Quickly, I pulled my trousers overtop making sure that nothing underneath was visible. Everything was fine until I started walking and the pants kept slipping down inside my trousers. To tackle this problem, I had to routinely re-adjust and pull them up which was irritating and weird. *I guess sports are off at break time,* I thought to myself, knowing full well that the movement would provoke the need for constant re-adjustment which, in turn, would cause questions to be asked. The safest thing was to do as little as possible throughout the day.

We arrived at the school at 9:10 am, and as usual, my mum left me to face the wrath of the teacher for my tardiness instead of coming in and explaining the situation herself with an apology. Aside from the initial bollocking I had to endure, things seemed to be moving smoothly enough. First period ended without a hitch and break time was upon us. I spent most of the time sitting on the patio nearest my classroom playing Pogs with Steve till he left to play tag, then I cracked out a summer sales Argos catalogue I had stolen from home and perved at all the cool photos of the videogames I would never own. Yet another bone of contention in my house, where all my friends were given all the latest toys and video games they asked for; meanwhile, my parents insisted 'video games would rot my brain'. I grew up a very jealous child because of this, but due to their obstinate refusal of anything I found fun, my desires were never quenched. In recent years, I've read many an article that states that science has proven that kids who played videogames in younger years have a much better ability to solve problems and are actually smarter for it. I, of course, now remind them of this fact as often as I can to rub salt in an open wound. However, like most of their attitudes, they have grown callous and refuse to issue any form of apology and, in fact, remain steadfast and unyielding in their wrong belief that Christmas and birthdays are for giving gifts the giver wants to give, rather that ever taking into account something that the receiver might get maximum enjoyment out of or want. Anyway, I digress.

Break time ended, and I made my way back to class and waited. Five minutes passed and I was still alone. Eventually, Anna Campbell walked in and grabbed her backpack.

"Yo, what's going on? Where is everyone?" I asked starting to worry.

"In the hall, it's PE today, remember? I just came back to get my kit," Anna replied and swiftly made her way back to the assembly hall. My mouth went dry as the realisation of P.E class set in. I gingerly made my way to the hall, seeing the gym apparatus was all in position. This was not a drill. Kids started to file out of the changing rooms and into the hall. As the changing room emptied, I saw Kevin was sat on the bench inside putting on some ancient daps. Pretty quickly the sound of heavy footsteps made their way towards the door.

"You're in luck, Kevin, there's one pair of shorts in the lost property; you can wear these," Mrs Harris said, chucking a pair of slightly soiled looking P.E shorts at Kevin's face.

"Um, Miss Harris, I've forgot my kit too, I'll just sit P.E out for today, alright," I said in a stuttered nervous manner.

"Don't be silly, you know the drill, you'll do it in your underpants," she huffed, filling the room with her coffee breath.

"I can't do that, Miss Harris, not today," I yelped.

"Why not?" she replied sternly. I sighed.

"Look, is there anymore P.E shorts in lost property?" I begged.

"No, you heard me say to Kevin that was the last pair, he got here first, I'm sorry. You know the rules, just take comfort in the fact that in the grand scheme of things, this'll be forgotten before you know it," she replied with a cruel smirk riddled upon her massive face.

"You don't understand," I frantically pleaded.

"No, you don't understand, if you're not out there in 5 minutes, I'm sending you straight to the Miss Butterworth's (the Headmistress) office."

I moaned and looked over at Kevin who was wearing the same cruel smirk on his stupid face.

"Listen Kevin, buddy, what would it take to let me have your shorts," I said kindly, trying desperately to manipulate him into a gesture of good will by offering him a metaphorical blank cheque.

"Um, we become best friends till we finish St Paul's School in year 6," he said eagerly.

"Okay," I replied cautiously weighing up my options.

"And I get to eat all your snacks and lunches for the next year!" he continued.

"Right," I responded.

"…and we hang out every day at every break and lunch time for the duration," he masterfully added playing his cards as best as he could. I thought for a second. I may not have liked this kid, but I was an honest man and didn't want to lie just to make a trade.

"Never gonna happen!" I replied gruffly like a cool Dirty Harry and Jack Bauer's love child.

"Suit yourself," Said Kevin, gleefully smiling at my alternative. He then licked his hand and ruffled my hair before skipping out towards the hall like a special needs fairy.

"Great," I said under my breath, and sat back down on the bench trying desperately to think of ways to stall the inevitable. Miss Harris poked her head around through the changing room door.

"Get a move on, Michael. I'm not gonna ask you again!" she scolded.

"I'm just popping to the loo, I'll be right back!" I fumed back scampering towards the toilet. Inside the cubicle, I paced up and down desperately trying to wile the hour away. Five minutes later, I was still there. *Well, might as well take a pee since I'm here,* I thought to myself and pulled my trousers down, the panties just dropped conveniently due to their large size. My peeing was quickly shaken as I jumped from the sound of Miss Harris pounding on the door.

"Time's up! Get out here now!" she ordered.

I peered down and saw that in the scare of the interruption I had managed to pee all over the pink frillies.

"Nooooo!" I gasped loudly, as the added insult to injury increased when the stain became more prevalent as the dark wet patches started to accumulate at the front of the panties.

"Michael, you have 3 seconds!" Miss Harris continued.

"Alright!" I screamed back. There was only a plywood door separating us.

"3, 2, 1," Miss Harris counted down, and I swung the door open revealing my tragic state.

"Oh boy!" Miss Harris remarked chuckling to herself.

"Well out you go," she said forcibly pushing me through the two doors separating the changing room from the main hall. I stood in horror in my white polo shirt, and pink frillies as my class quickly stopped their activity to join in united scoffing and mockery of my misfortune. Miss Harris, eventually, told them to calm down and proceeded to make our class run laps around the hall to warm up. This was the most difficult activity for me as once again the vigorous movement couldn't be done without clinging on to the panties to keep them from dropping which only added further embarrassment as kids began to mock me for holding onto them tightly like they were precious to me. Forty-five long minutes later, P.E was finished. I sprinted to the changing room to put my trousers on. I don't know why, I knew full well my dignity was a lost cause as this horror story would be told in weeks to come. Hell, it may even be a cautionary tale that primary school students tell to their peers to this day.

It was tough but as always in childhood you learn to adapt, overcome and survive the taunts of your peers till it becomes a distant memory replaced by more current embarrassing tales of woe. Obviously, rebuilding one's street cred after such an incident is a difficult task, but I gutted it out as I always did and rolled with a punch. I'm often amazed at the amount of torture the human spirit can endure without crumbling. But just like some of the survivors of Auschwitz have chosen to forgive their captors, I have chosen to forgive my mockers. Of course, if any of those mockers choose to taunt me after the offer of forgiveness has been bestowed, I shall disembowel them where they stand, but no one could blame me for that.

Chapter 10
Manna from Kevin

One of the biggest injustices I faced during my formative years in St Paul's School was to do with packed lunches and snacks. Whilst my peers scoffed down peanut butter and jam, chocolate spread or marshmallow fluff sandwiches and were treated to Mars Bars, Snickers or Walkers Crisps for snack time, I was sent to school with a sensible but joyless tuna and sweetcorn sandwich for lunch and a carrot for snack time. I spent half my home life petitioning for a more exciting menu, even going as far to write a shopping list for my mum, to take some of the work out of it. I was savagely ignored, and my basic human rights were rejected by their pompous, contemptible and hardened hearts. Honestly, their stance was over the top. I even got told off for once spending my pocket money on an ice cream from the ice cream van without their permission. Naturally, after years of being ground down with jealousy of my fellow students and anger at my parents I started to lose faith. I mean think about it, what 8-year-old is going to swap me their Mars Bar for my carrot? In my last few years at St Paul's I had even taken to throwing my lunch away on a daily basis in a Mahatma Gandhi style hunger strike protest. Of course, when my parents got wind of this, I was viciously disciplined, but this only spurred me on to do it more, though I did try to hide it from my parents from then on. By the end of the year, I think I had disposed of enough carrots to feed a family of reindeer all through winter, and enough tuna and sweetcorn sandwiches to endanger the species and lay waste to an entire Nebraskan harvest like a pack of locusts. All was going well with my hunger strike till I was spotted by a friend of my parents, throwing away my sandwiches at the end of a school day. This lady, a massive busybody who had always been a pebble in my shoe since I spent a week living at her house while my parents went on vacation once (I say living but the experience was more like dying), ratted me out that evening, presumably with a very satisfied smile on her face. I remember every detail of that evening, the sound of the phone, my dad's cross voice, a 'word' being had in my room, and a spanking to end all spankings. At one point, as my dad was laying down the law, he explained what action he was going to take.

"I'm gonna give you a spank for throwing your sandwiches away again, followed by a second spank for lying to us and telling us you wouldn't do it again!" he said like he was being perfectly reasonable.

"I wasn't lying, I was kidding," I desperately tried to reason back with a terrified smile on my face. "It's your fault if you can't take a joke" I added. In hindsight, my behaviour was pretty embarrassing. Meanwhile, my mum sat silently by like a cold statue who merely came to adjudicate the situation. Needless to say I was spanked rotten that night. Sadly that was not the end of my struggles, as immediately after spanking me, my parents demanded I hug them whilst they told me 'they loved me' as this was meant to remind the child that they were still cared for. Apparently, it was a parenting technique they picked up from a book they read on the matter. They learnt a lot of awful advice from that book, and if I ever find out what it was called, I shall make it my mission in life to find every copy and pulp it, next, find the author, break every bone in his body and then flog him to death. To add further insult to injury, this enforced strict healthy food diet that only I was subjected to only served to make me crave junk even more. To this end, I spent my more adult years in my 20s gorging myself on anything sweet or fattening to make up for the constant denial as a child. This was the same principle Michael Jackson once lived by and why he created Neverland Ranch as a way of making up for his lost childhood. Of course, we both went over the top due to the lack of parental restraint in later years; Consequently, he was convicted of being a paedophile, and I was mistaken for a whale. I was a fatty all through my 20s, and it took till my 30th birthday to finally regain some self-control and the discipline needed to lose the excess pounds, all of this which would never have happened if I were allowed a normal lunch like my peers in the first place. Clearly, the blame lies one hundred percent solely on my parents. To this day, we are still ironing out the creases in our relationship and trying to bandage the fragile rift between us.

One day, during school, we were approaching snack time and everyone was finishing up their work to play. Everyone but John Day, of course, who wanted to stay in, do more reading and learn more like a dork. Academia was his only friend. As everyone else dispersed to go play, they walked past the snack crate grabbing their snack on their way out. I was still sitting due to an ill-fated attempt to wipe some snot that I picked from my nose, under the desk... a habit I had formed at the beginning of the school year and by now made the bottom of the desk look like the cocoon chambers in the Alien movies. By the time I had sorted out the complications, everyone had left the room save for John whose face was buried in a calculus book. I walked past the snack crate, and had to do a double take when I saw a packet of Cadburys Animals Bites left unclaimed just sitting there. As with Gollum and the ring, I was drawn to the Animal Bites seductive powers, until I was overcome. Naturally, I checked my surroundings first, then snatched the bag and consumed the contents of its sweet chocolatey goodness as quickly as I could, almost to the point of choking. Afterwards, I surreptitiously made my way over to the next classroom and disposed of the packet in their bin. Finally, I wiped away any residue of crumbs and chocolate from the side of my mouth to hide any trace of evidence and felt very confident I had conducted the perfect crime. 10 minutes passed and everyone had come in from break to continue classes. During the period between break time and lunch, we studied the lives of the Victorian era. This would have been boring, although fortunately, we were at the dawn of the horrible histories books which actually managed to make history interesting for a change. Sadly, these books were not on the academic reading list, so we would usually hide them inside our texts books to read at our own leisure. Richard Slate was at the front of the class showing off a camera that he had made using a can of coke... He was talking about how cameras were first invented in the Victorian era, and that this primitive style of technology is probably how they did it. Obviously, not with a coke can, but he got the point across. Next, Kevin got up and began to talk about his self-made black death mask (which was really just a pair of swimming goggles with a beak made from cardboard sellotaped sloppily to it), but he was quickly shut down by Miss Harris for citing erroneous dates and facts about the black death plague masks, which, in fact, belonged in the 14th Century.

Well done, Kevin, I thought sarcastically, *only off by 400 years*. The most amusing part of it was when Kevin refused to listen to Miss Harris and carried on talking. She grabbed the beak and pulled it forwards till it snapped off and the attached goggles ricocheted back to Kevin's eyes. For a moment he stood shocked. But then, realizing no one, least of all the teacher, was going to give him the attention he desired, he sat down quietly next to Richard (who had cut his finger on the coke can and was desperately trying to hold back the tears).

Other kids showed off their inventions relating to the era including a telephone which was merely two cups joined by a piece of string and some piss poor hand drawn stamps which would not hold up under scrutiny at Royal Mail. I can tell you that much for free.

As the class moved onwards, I soon forgot about the Animal Bites I had pilfered at break time and the worry about getting caught barely registered in my brain. The bell soon rang for lunch, and as standard, we kids started making our way outside with our lunch boxes in hand. It was at this point that I made my way to the door only to be stopped by the sound of Kevin's shouting.

"Where is it?"

"Where is what?" Miss Harris responded, annoyed that this question would now eat into her lunch break in the teachers' room. This was where teachers would gather together and regale each other with stories of the most annoying student that day and their hatred for him/her (most days I'm sure it was Kevin). For them, it was the only bastion and 'safe area' where they could vent all their pent-up irritations.

"My Animal Bites? Somebody's taken them!" Kevin squealed like a pig.

"Are you sure, Kevin? Are you sure you didn't just eat them at snack time, I mean they were in the snack box," an impatient Miss Harris replied.

"No I was saving them to have with my lunch," he woofed back, a cross frown beginning to crease up on his forehead.

"Right well, you still have your lunch, right? I'm afraid you'll have to make do," Miss Harris finished. A brief sigh of relief left my lips as I stood by the door nervously. Glad that the line of enquiry was closed. I opened the door and began to walk out. As the door was half way closed, I heard three little words which changed the course of time (for me anyway).

"Michael ate them," John said, looking up from an astrophysics book momentarily, throwing me under a bus. *Bastard*, I thought, my back leg still holding the door open. I realised I needed to deal with this now instead of worrying all lunch time about the repercussions.

I gingerly walked back towards the classroom to face Kevin and Miss Harris.

"Michael, did you eat Kevin's Animal Bites snack?" Harris asked sternly. I coughed anxiously.

"Uhhh, I dunno, I can't remember," I whispered dryly, my mouth running low on saliva. I did know, and the truth was written on my face.

"Michael, John is not that sort of person to make this stuff up, so I'm gonna ask you once again, and I want an honest answer," Miss Harris said, cruelly repeating her line of interrogation. I knew she wouldn't let this drop.

"I might have, I can't, well, it's possible, I just, not sure," I stuttered whilst hot prickles chased up the back of my neck. I was in full on 'shit myself' mode. This was not a drill.

"Yes or no, Michael?" Miss Harris growled.

"Okay," I replied, still being indecisive.

"You've got three seconds before I march you to the headmistress' office!" Harris screeched, "3…2…1."

"Yes, probably, yes, I ate them, sorry, I thought they were mine," I quickly responded, frightened as a kitten by this point. I also knew they weren't mine, but I took my chances and hoped she wouldn't open another line of enquiry to check the veracity of this statement.

"You thought they were yours?" she asked less tense than before.

Shit, I thought to myself.

"Yes, I thought they were mine," I decided to lie breaking my thin moral code, which only really came into observance when death was on the line by this age.

"You thought they were yours?" she repeated again, clearly not buying my utterly crap poker face. Panicking, I backtracked a bit, again, a rookie mistake.

"They could have been mine," I wistfully replied with a jokey smile on my face, hoping to play the abashed clown card to calm the situation and play it off as a silly mistake that could be forgiven with a 'oh you rascal' comment and a mushing of hair. Sadly, Miss Harris wasn't having any of it and continued to stare at me with fury in her eyes.

"Does your mum usually pack Cadbury's Animal Bites for you for snack time?" Miss Harris carried on.

"No, she gives him a carrot for snack every day," Kevin rudely interrupted with a smug smile and chopsy tone.

Shut up, Kevin, I thought to myself, almost loudly enough to say the words through my gritted teeth.

"Is this true, Michael?" harked Miss Harris with a hard-nosed counter line of questioning. I shrugged my shoulders.

"Sometimes, I guess," I returned, trying to remain as ambiguous as possible.

"Right," Harris finished abruptly and walked out of the room leaving both Kevin and I wondering if that was the end of it. I walked over to where John Day was still sitting.

"Well done, knob head!" I said furiously, giving John a charley horse on his right leg. Annoyingly he didn't react to the pain, but instead, turned to me and said in a patronising fashion:

"You only have yourself to blame," then smirked and nonchalantly turned the page of his boffin book. Moments later, Miss Harris returned. I stood to attention like a naughty boy who had just been caught in the middle of mischief. Kevin, meanwhile, lay sprawled across the desk, only lifting his head (which dangled off the edge) in acknowledgement till Harris spoke.

"I've just spoken to both of your parents on the telephone," she casually dropped, watching for our reactions. It felt like the announcement of lie detector results on Jeremy Kyle.

"Kevin, the phone call proved that the Animal Bites were in fact yours. Michael…" I could feel my heart racing, "the phone call to your mum shows…" Miss Harris paused for dramatic effect, "you were lying."

I gulped. Whatever we were planning to learn that afternoon after lunch had now been superseded by the need for me to focus on writing my last will and testament as I knew a thrashing was awaiting me at home.

"I think you should apologise," Miss Harris said still cross. Shamefully, I bowed my head and fell into line.

"Sorry, Kevin," I whispered, I wasn't sorry, just sorry I got caught and maybe sorry for the future murder of John Day. No, no, I wouldn't be sorry about that either, who am I kidding. I contemplated for a moment running away after school and living life as a drifter, but no matter how glamorously I dressed it up in my mind, I knew it would only end in living on the streets like a bum. To rub salt in an open wound, when class returned, Ben Baker took my seat and leaned back, gripping on the bottom of the desk for stability. No sooner had he done this that he levelled his chair and immediately retracted his hand with a scream.

"Yuk!" he yelled, so the whole class would observe the incident. Next, he peaked under the table at what he touched and discovered my labyrinthine mess of dried and wet snot collected over the course of the year, and immediately exposed me as the perpetrator. I desperately scrambled around trying to hush him up or change the subject in vain. This was incredibly humiliating but ultimately I didn't really care. The die had been cast, and the day had been a massive right off. The rest of the day flew past (which it always does when you don't want it to) To add further stress to my already Macbeth like plagued mind, in those days, my dad didn't return home till about 8 pm from work. I'd have to anxiously wait several hours after coming home in fear to face my decided punishment. H P. Lovecraft once wrote: "The oldest and strongest emotion of mankind is fear, and the oldest and strongest kind of fear is fear of the unknown." I think he hit the nail on the head. Eventually, my dad returned and it was like Groundhog Day, except instead of getting two spanks, I was rewarded 3 for the fruit of my labours. One for thieving, one for lying and one for luck, to really push the point home.

Chapter 11
Panto

Now let me warn you ahead of time, this is going to be a rather brief chapter. I've not got much to say on the matter. I don't believe the subject deserves much, if any credence and I shall not waste my time discussing it longer than I feel necessary. In short, I absolutely hate Panto (Pantomimes). Unfortunately, I was exposed to it more often than I'd liked to remember during my primary school education as it was a bi-annual treat for us kids. How on any planet one could label a trip to the Panto a treat is beyond me. As for where school is concerned, I struggle to find any academic value in a Panto either. I know people will say, "Oh lighten up, it's just a bit of fun, Michael." But it's not 'a bit of fun', not any fun at all. People may say, "Well, it's meant for kids." I can tell you, as a kid at the time, I found it very patronising, immature and thoroughly unenjoyable. It was basically bubble gum for the brain of two-year olds. Now, in all fairness, I stole that phrase from a column I read from a film critic about the movie Space Jam upon its release in 1996, but it's something that stuck in my head ever since and I feel can be applied to Pantos too. Probably even more to be honest, although I'd love to hear this critic's review of Dick Whittington.

Twice a year we were mandatorily shipped out by Bennett's Coaches for a lengthy two-hour journey to Birmingham to sit through an excruciating 3-hour long boreathon of annoying jokes and innuendos. Now I'm not saying I have the finger on the pulse of comedy, and obviously it's all pretty subjective, but for me, it was one massive cringefest of has-been actors desperately trying to claw their way back out of obscurity. What they didn't seem to understand is that Panto is and always will be desperate and undignified, which, in turn, will only serve to worsen their career and cheapen any gravitas and clout they had before. There is such a thing as retiring gracefully.. I knew that as a child and I was shocked that they didn't as adults.

Fortunately, I've since blocked most of those memories out, and I can't for the life of me remember a single plot from any of the Pantos. I saw, mainly 'cuz I think the plot was merely a device for packing in as many camp jokes and innuendos as possible, so it didn't really matter (in their eyes) that the story had no substance.

The only joy I ever got at a Panto experience was on the return journey one time. Patrick McDougal was having another lover's tiff with his girlfriend Xenia who was continually switching back and forth between him and Andrew Murphy at this point. Steve and I took this opportunity to berate Patrick and kick him whilst he was down. It seems cruel looking back, and it was, but Steve was Patrick's brother, and I was Steve's best friend, so it was the natural order of things. I was also happy as this particular time I was staying over at Steve's house for the night so our teasing could last all through till dawn the next morning. And it did. Looking back, we were bastards back then, but those sorts of experiences really bond friends when you're a kid and naturally Patrick would reciprocate the abuse on a day when either Steve or I had had some bad news. It was the making of a man, and to this day, we're all still mates. Steve has moved to Swindon and has 3 kids. Patrick resides in a mental institute in Slough and is up for review in 2022. I'm joking.

Chapter 12
Cycling Improficiency

One morning, I went into class and stood before me were two ladies I recognised. Their attendance seemed completely out of place. It was Judy Hacker, a heavy-set women with thick 80s spectacles and curly granny hair (yunno that hairstyle that 90% of women adopt in their mid-40s early 50s that screams 'I've given up on trying to be attractive'). The second lady, Joan Armstrong, was a skinny, bony short POW looking lady who sported a short manish hairstyle, like Keanu Reeves in 'Speed'. For some reason, her hair and face always reminded me of a ladybird, but not in a cute or delightful way, just in the way her hair sat on her head, like a swimming cap. I knew both of the ladies from my parents' church, but I couldn't for the life of me understand what they were doing here. It soon became clear when they explained that they were both cycling proficiency examiners, which threw me for a loop as I had always just assumed they were boring old housewives. Not that cycling proficiency examiner is a cool job or anything, in fact, looking back, much like the test, it probably doesn't mean anything. I can't imagine any education or special training is required except basic knowledge of the high way code, which everyone learns to acquire a driving license later in life anyway.

When it got announced we'd be doing our cycling proficiency that day, most everyone was down for it. Most everyone, except Gene Colins and Kevin Blankenhorn who were still using stabilisers at age ten and were now terrified their dirty little secret would be exposed. I, on the other hand, like most of my class was confident on two wheels. My dad had taught me to cycle at around age 4; he was good like that. I know I've knocked him a lot in this book, but for the things that matter like teaching me to ride a bike, swim and drive, he's always been there, at least until he could find someone more qualified to do the job.

Judy and Joan started handing sheets out around the class that covered the basic road safety laws regarding riding a bicycle. It was about 5 minutes learning but thanks to those members of the class who were slow and barely had any comprehension of the English language. (I'm looking at you Kevin) we had to slow the process down to explain simple words like 'indicate', 'accelerate' and 'blind spot'.

After break time, we all went and grabbed our bikes from the stands and were ushered down the street towards 'Dugdale Road.'. As we made our way, I checked out everyone's bikes. Some took my fancy like the green Raleigh with cool black hubcaps with green spray paint flashes on them, owned by Tim Colins (a kid who looked exactly like one of the riddlers from a 1990s kids show called 'The Riddlers' about some extremely ugly muppets who live in the woods). The piece de resistance, however, was a bike called the 'Street wolf' also by Raleigh that looked like what would occur if the tech team behind the Airwolf helicopter from the show Airwolf decided to make a bicycle. It was badass and even had one of the first cycle computers built in to read the speed of the bike, as if a 10-year-old kid would need to monitor this in case he was breaching the national speed limit of 60 mph by pumping his legs too fast. Still if anyone could do it, it would have been the bike's owner, Keith Rockerfella. Not too likeable, but with a devil-may-care, badass approach to life, Keith may not have had many friends, but he made up for it in bad boy appeal. Gene on the other hand, had a bike that looked like it was picked out of the fisher price section of the Argos catalogue. It had a big red bell on the handlebars as well as a basket attacked to the front, presumably where he kept his dollies. I couldn't tell if the tyres were real or plastic. Kevin was pushing along what could only be described as an abortion of a bike. It was in essence a kids racing bike, and as such had a large thin wheel at the front; however, its back wheel had been taken off and replaced with a smaller rubber BMX wheel which, in turn, made it look like a makeshift Penny-farthing. The rear wheel, which had attached to it two cheap scrap metal stabilisers on either side at the back, trailed a collection of tin cans on a string like a 'just married' car. In an effort to gain some cool clout, Kevin had stuck some bicycle beads on the front spokes that had come straight from a packet of cheerios that morning, as well as attached bright florescent stickers of generic 90s words like 'Rad', 'Bad and 'Cool' on the frame. He thought it looked boss. In reality, it looked like Frankenstein's monster.

We made our way to Dugdale road where Judy and Joan had to calm down the more rambunctious kids from pulling wheelies and racing down the road to show off their longest skids. Finally, they got everyone in tow, though they had wasted a good half of the lesson pissing about chasing after Keith, who kept playing them for a fool, slowing down, then speeding up just as they got close enough to catch him. Judy and Joan then directed kids one at a time to cycle down Dugdale road, turning into the left-hand slip road and bringing the bike to a stop, all whilst insisting one made the correct checks and indications along the way. Ben went first, then Alex and John followed etc., going through the alphabet by surname and checking them off one by one. Soon it was Kevin's turn. He plopped onto his bike completely neglecting to check his blind spot, and set off down the road. We could all see and hear the tin cans that jangled and chased him down the path. Stupidly, he missed the junction and kept speeding along. Eventually, he turned left, without indication into a nearby car park exit. Joan and Judy chased after him frantically as he disappeared out of sight. The rest of us followed curious to see the outcome. Next, we heard an almighty crash and thud, at which point, we all sped up our chase…. Joan and Judy out of fear, the rest of us out of morbid amusement. We eventually found Kevin face down on the ground, heavily panting to hold back the tears. Judy and Joan helped him up to his feet and offered him some water. His shirt and trousers were torn to ribbons, and he had a few scratches on his hands and a cut knee. But overall, he was alright. Fortunately for him, one of the rules of taking part in cycling proficiency is that we all wore helmets, an option I've never chosen since because they're not cool. I think that day, however, that helmet saved Kevin's life. He sat on a bench nearby continuing to catch his breath, posing like a wounded battle soldier, holding his tattered helmet in his hands like the guy on the Black Hawk Down poster. Alas, unlike the soldier, there was no heroism here, just a train wreck of a person who fell off his train wreck of a bike. We later found out that one of Kevin's tin cans that were trailing the bike had got caught on the lip of a drain and buckled the entire bike backwards jerking him over the handlebars. In fairness, he got off lightly since he could have gone straight through the window of a car exiting the car park. The bike, however, was a complete write off.

Soon it came to my turn and my confident ability to ride my bike meant I performed the whole routine perfectly no handed. I even turned the corner without touching the handlebars, waving arrogantly at my peers who were quite clearly impressed by my skills, before bringing my bike to a complete and safe stop. I felt like a boss, and in all honesty, I was. It was a good time to be alive.

Finally, we came to the end of the register save for one candidate, Richard Slate. He rode an ugly brown bike with thin wheels that looks like he must have inherited from his dad in the 1940s. It was similar to the one used in the famous Ridley Scott Hovis TV advert of yesteryear. As he set off, we could all see he too was confident about his abilities and made sure we knew that by riding with his chin raised like some pompous twat looking down on the peasants. Again, he sped down the road no handed, showing off his skills, but trying to top mine by clapping on either side of the bike, then doing some arm flicks which flowed from one arm to the other like a miniature Mexican wave, like a buffoon. I nudged Steve in annoyance of what I was seeing.

"What a prat, right!?" I whispered. I wasn't really worried about Richard stealing my thunder, my clout was already sky high and his was set in stone six feet under. My annoyance quickly changed to elation, however, when Richard, who was still speeding along at a fairly nice speed, cycled over one of those drains with the vertical (or horizontal, depending how you look at it) slits in them, and the front wheel got stuck and buckled throwing Richard off, then somersaulting onto his battered body that was lying on the floor.

"MEDIC!" I screamed comically, causing everyone to burst into hysterics. I even saw a small chuckle erupt on Joan and Judy's face before containing themselves and catching up with Richard who was lying still on the ground, eyes closed like he was actually dead. They lifted to tattered bike off his carcass. We all rushed down the street to get a good view, peering over his small frame.

"Hypochondriac," I said, which landed with mixed reviews. In fairness, it was a bit early. He hadn't opened his eyes yet and might have actually been dead for all I knew. Moments later, he coughed and wheezed, opening his eyes. He had only winded himself this time, but, of course, that didn't stop him from crying. Then he spotted his bike on the side, or what was left of the crumpled mess that once was. This, in turn, brought on more tears as he limped to his feet.

"Give him room, give him room," Judy said.

"Oh, my dad is gonna kill me," Richard whined kicking his bike in frustration.

"Hard luck, mate, you were doing so well too!" I said, a slight cheeky glint in my eye, as I patted him on his back.

"Oh piss off, Michael!" he replied and did a pathetic kick in my direction, knowing full well I was being facetious.

"Well, that was unnecessary," I contested, to wind him up further.

We made our way back to school and locked our bikes up.

"Bin's over there, mate," I said to Richard as I pointed towards the skip that had been initially hired by the school to dispose of the old playground set. Richard thumped me on the arm, I just laughed. Getting back to class we all chatted among ourselves about how we thought we did as Judy and Joan handed back our score sheets.

That day, everyone passed, with exception of Richard Slate and Kevin and me!? I looked at the page in horror and confusion. All I could figure is that because Judy and Joan knew me from outside the school they didn't want to look partial and, therefore, made an example out of me. This was not fair, and I quickly took up my bone of contention with them. They explained (wrongly) that because I had taken both my hands off the handle bars and performed the entire test this way, I was not in control of the bike at all times. I fought this unjust cause till I was blue in the face, arguing that I had done all my checks, indications and observations perfectly, and whilst their argument may have held water with tits like Richard who proved they were in over their head riding no handed, the fact that I had not made a mistake showed I was in complete control. My appeal was savagely rejected by the courts of Judy and Joan, as their stone hearts grew more and more stubborn with every reason I gave. That day, I went home with a bitter taste in my mouth, a bitter taste that has yet to be resolved.

I occasionally bump into Judy and Joan in town and bring up the subject, hoping that the years may have softened their hearts and they may repeal their damning judgment and offer me some retroactive vindication. Even when I explain that I have now been cycling for 28 years and have not had a serious crash their hearts turn to stone and all the love leaves their faces.

Chapter 13
School Play

In our penultimate year at St Paul's School, we were tasked to perform a school play. It was Mrs Rudley's brainchild, and she made that very clear, like some selfish, show off child wanting to direct all the praise her way. In a way, because I don't think she could have babies (she was barren as Mars), this was her baby. The play was called 'Along Came Man' and dealt with all the themes that were popular in the 90s like saving the rainforest/nature etc. It was a massive riff on the movies 'Ferngully: The Last Rainforest' and 'Free Willy', which had recently come out. Movies that James Cameron has been accused of riffing on for Avatar, despite having written Avatar back in the mid-80s. I'm sure, given the chance, Mrs Rudley would have accused James Cameron of riffing off her play too, but alas, he was not present on any of the performance days. The play was also a musical. Although basic, I'll have to admit it had some pretty catchy lyrics that have been branded into my mind since. I'm sure in Mrs Rudley's mind her songs were akin to Michael Jackson's Earth Song.

It wasn't the first school play I took part in. Back in my first year at St Paul's, we students were all dressed up in wedding gear, and were forced (under duress) to perform a marriage ceremony, in which I (playing the Vicar, essentially wearing a black dress with a dog collar) married Ben Adams to Amy Price. It was meant to be a lesson in the dynamics of a Christian wedding, but it turned out to be a lesson in humiliation and humility. I don't remember Ben and Amy every getting divorced, so my plan is to go to their real-life weddings and stick my hand up when the question is asked whether 'anyone knows of any reason why they should not be joined together in holy matrimony' for a laugh. The only other play which I have no idea what it was about that I took part in before 'Along Came Man' was one where I dressed as a robin for some reason and was begrudgingly coerced into wearing brown tights for the role, which naturally incurred a hefty fine of a week or twos worth of bullying, thereafter. In fairness, 'Along Came Man' was a lot more humane. I played a lumberjack, which was more befitting of the masculine man that I would become.

The play was split into 3 parts switching between nature and man's progression in technology etc., which, in turn, damaged the wildlife. So it would go, nature, Along Came Man, detrimental effects on nature, Along Came Man 2, further detrimental effects on nature, Along Came Man 3, the death of nature and lack of harvests, mineral ores etc. leading to the end of mankind. Then it would be all summed up at the end with a touching lesson learned and a singsong with all characters on stage learning to live together in harmony. It was pretty hippie but it did the job. Of course, Mrs Rudley absolutely bummed herself over it and took its conception to delivery with a ridiculous amount of solemn reverence. Let's be honest, as a school play, it was probably a solid 3.5 out of 5, but it was no Die Hard. Having done research for this book I discovered that the play was in fact purchased from a company that specialises in Primary School Plays called Faber Music and written by a woman named Lin Marsh. Annoyingly I've also had to pay the £75 + VAT licensing fee just to mention it in this book. Let's hope I sell enough copies to at least break even. Thanks a lot Mrs Rudley!

Anyway, I don't really have many memories of my role, other than I was in Along Came Man 3 right before the death of nature. I wore shorts and a T-shirt and marched around a tree miming axing it down. We had a song to sing too, but I don't remember the lyrics. There was, however, a song I do remember verbatim called 'The Age of Technology' which came midway through the play just before the intermission. The lyrics I shall write here as a device to shamelessly bulk up my word count.

This is the age, the age of technology.
This is the age of fun.
Welcome to the age, the age of technology.
Something for everyone.

Computers there to train you.
Hi Fi to entertain you.
No need to use your brain you may say.
But we like our world this way.
(Lengthy accent on the way at the end).

I think the only reason I remember this song more than mine was because the scene involved a girl I had a crush on at the time named Kelly Stark, so I used to come to rehearsals early to stare at her, and that strength of focus, which I lacked in my studies, was all spent on perving. Kelly Stark later grew up to be a lesbian, so it seems I was barking up the wrong tree all along. Ah well, such is life sometimes.

Chapter 14
The Diary of the Isle of Wight

It was our final year and miraculously the school had found it in their budget to take our entire class on an adventure week on the Isle of Wight at a pseudo summer camp where we would learn and do all sorts of outdoor activities. We were allowed to pack a week's worth of non-school uniform (our own clothes) and had to return a parentally signed permission slip that probably had some very thorough but concerning fine print waivers regarding child safety liability.

The trip sounded too good to be true, and it was, as once we were all on board the bus and the door were closed, the teachers read us a list of their demands (rules) for the trip. In fairness, most of the rules were to do with following the schedule, but a couple of them were there simply to put a damper on the whole week. Rules like, bedtime 8 pm and lights out and no talking by 9 pm, which I felt was far too early and wholly unfair. I had learnt by this age though that what I thought meant nothing to the teachers of St Paul's School, so I didn't bother fighting it. The last rule (which I think was created solely to break the spirit of the student trying to enjoy a week at camp free of the chains of traditional academia) was that every student had to keep a daily diary. As far as I was concerned, this was far too similar to school work as it required writing, which I hated. The teachers tried to make it fun by adding that we can write whatever we want in our diary, make it our own, as long as we did one. We had to hand it in at the end of the week, but they promised not to read it. They probably did breach that confidence and read it in the staff room during break for their own amusement but if they found anything in mine that they didn't like and tried to take it up with me, I'd remind them of their promise and explain that they betrayed my trust and that now I wasn't liable for a bollocking. They were. At the end of the school year, I remember the diary being returned to me like a convict gets his belongings returned from a prison guard after his sentence is up. I'll never know whether it was read by them or not, as the teacher may have had a good poker face.

The other day, I was routing around in my attic when I found it by chance in a dusty alcove after I cleared out a family of pigeons that had been nesting there like brood of bird Anne Franks. It's just sheer irony that I stumbled upon my diary at the same time. I've since given it a read and decided (because most of the teachers involved in that trip have probably already read it are dead, dying or just won't bother reading this book) to include it here. Therefore, what follows is an unedited, unabridged transcribed version of my Isle of Wight diary for your reading pleasure.

Isle of Wight Diary
Day One

This morning, we all got on the bus headed for the Isle of Wight. I sat next to Adam Blackburn and talked about bows and arrows. Kevin did such a smelly poo in the toilet that it stank out the whole bus for the duration of the bus trip till we reached the services for lunch and the driver had a 15-minute break to fumigate the bus. When we arrived at the bottom of England, we all took a ferry over to the Isle of Wight. Once we arrived there, we got on another bus that took us to the camp. The teachers then gave us our room assignments and told us we could take the evening off to explore. I am bunking with Gene, Adam, Richard, Ben, Andrew and Steven. Thank goodness I got put with at least a couple of my friends. I unpacked and went for a look around, but it was getting pretty dark, so I decided to head back to the room. As I was on my way back, I decided to peer through the window of one of the other bedrooms to see if I could have done better for myself room assignment wise. I wish I hadn't as I saw something I'll never forget. The room was empty save for Ben Baker who was in a fetal position on the floor with no trousers or pants on, and was seemingly tickling his bum hole. Part of me wants to share this information with a friend in order to make the burden more bearable, but the other part is confident it'll cause them nightmares for years to come, and I can't in good conscience inflict such horror upon them. Tonight's sleep will be troubled.

Day Two

This morning, we all met in the canteen for breakfast. There was lots of yummy sausages, eggs and bacon, as well as the more traditional toast and jam or cereal options. I treated myself to a full English, why not? I'm not driving. After breakfast, Adam and I walked back to our room to find Gene towelling himself after a shower. He was completely naked but, thankfully, had the due diligence to find a pair of pants to put on (albeit the pair he was wearing before the shower). I soon found out. Gene has only packed one pair of pants for the week, not on purpose, but had left them ready next to his bag as he was packing and just forgot. Classic Gene.

Adam, Steven and I then walked over to the Archery course where our first activity would begin. Here we met up with Sam, Ben and Adam Daniels who were bunking in a different room. Ben Baker was also there but had no idea I knew what I knew. I tried to avoid acting too awkward and I don't think he picked up on anything, although I did flinch when he tried to pat me on the back with those dirty fingers. I liked archery and I'm pretty good at it due to doing it every Thursday evening at a club that I go to. When we had finished, we went for lunch again in the canteen. I had fish and chips which wasn't as good as my local. I think the cooks need to buck up their ideas. I was sat with Steve and Adam, and we were talking about what was better, Aladdin or The Lion King. Adam and Steve both said The Lion King, but they're wrong. Aladdin is far better. That bit where the Genie takes Aladdin out of the cave and says he's down by one wish, and Aladdin's like "I don't think so, I didn't 'wish' anything", and the Genie's chin literally drops to the floor always has me laughing. After lunch, we played the wide game, 50 50 in. Kevin decided to change into a disgusting pair of spandex trousers and thermal that really accented his fat. At one point, Richard cheated, then got called out for it, then cried about it. Classic Richard. He was soon sent off by Mrs Rudley who sent him back to our room to calm down, at which point, Alex Carter said one of the funniest things I'll ever remember, "Apollo Richard, you are clear to land." It was perfect timing too as Richard was still just in earshot walking away at the time. So he definitely heard it. I had sausages and mash for dinner. Evening has now come, and I'm now writing this wretched diary minutes before we have to put the lights out for our ridiculous curfew. In fairness, today was fun, except for this part.

Day Three

Today, we did two cool activities. After breakfast, we were all taken to a nearby lake to kayak. The instruction period before hand went on far too long as Kevin kept refusing to put his life jacket on, claiming he could swim the Atlantic Ocean, so this lake was no worry for him. Kevin is an idiot; he didn't even pass his 10-meter swimming badge at the swimming pool last year, so I was sure he was just showing off. This was made abundantly clear when his boat capsized and even with his mandatory life jacket on by this point, he couldn't control his buoyancy for splashing around in a panic too much. Eventually, one of the lifeguards pulled his floundering fat body out of the water, and we all laughed as he coughed up half the lake and sat wheezing on the bench. Steve and I paddled out beyond the allowable limit, but swiftly got told off by the lifeguard and returned to an inch within it. I don't know what their problem was, or what they thought was going to happen? Was Jason Voorhees going to pop out and snatch us? In their defence, they had just pulled Kevin out when he was bobbing upside down, so I guess they just didn't want any more surprises. After paddling around for 2 hours and the odd spontaneous water fight, everyone vs Richard Slate, which he was not keen on, but had no choice, we all went to lunch. I sat with Sam and Steve, and we discussed the latest series of Teenage Mutant Ninja Turtles, our favourite show of all time, ever. After lunch, we all got into a minibus and went to the beach. It was nice and sunny today so that was cool. I tried convincing Kevin to show me some more of his swimming skills by betting him he couldn't swim to the other side, but he wouldn't oblige because he said he would get told off. I tried using my best powers of persuasion saying I'd take the rap for it, and it was only a brief 2 miles unlike the 4,000 miles of the

Atlantic Ocean he swore he could swim earlier that day. He wasn't up for it though and said he had got tangled up in one of the strings in the lifejacket that morning that forced him to thrash around trying to untie it and that's why it 'looked' like he was drowning but wasn't. The life jacket didn't have any strings by the way. Eventually, I gave up and Kevin just sat there like a flabby dead weight making sandcastles and then smashing them over and then repeating the process. Ellie Crawford asked me to apply sun tan lotion to her back as she couldn't reach, which I felt a little weird about since she is going out with Ben Baker, but she's fairly attractive and Ben is a bit of an arse so I said yes. We headed back from the beach at 5 pm and all got dressed back into our normal clothes. Afterwards, we went for dinner. I ate spaghetti bolognaise and had banana fritters for pudding, neither of which were anything to write home about, but I'll mention them here. It's near bedtime again and Gene has lost a sock. Fortunately, he brought more with him (unlike underpants).

Day Four

Last night after finishing my diary entry, I witnessed one of the quickest, simplest, most obvious yet hilarious comebacks I've ever heard in my life. We were all in our room save for Ben Rickets. Suddenly, Ben burst in through our door and loudly and proudly asked in an accusatory fashion, "Alright, who's being gay!?" in a poor attempt to appear like the cool tough guy. Andrew who was shuffling through some clothes in his drawer quickly turned around in a disgruntled fashion and said, "You are." I cried myself to sleep last night with laughter, at least until I was heard by one of the teachers at around 11 pm, and they gave me a massive telling off. Eventually, I practically had to suffocate myself to stop laughing, but I'm alive today so all is well. Richard peed the bed last night. Thankfully, he brought his rubber sheets from home. Alas it didn't stop the smell. This morning, the teachers moved him into their room for the rest of duration of the trip to shield his fragile ego and from the onslaught of mockery of his peers. Today for breakfast, I had porridge which tasted like it was made out of massive dust particles. We then did one awesome activity and one crap one. Thankfully, the crap one, orienteering (or, as I like to call it, borienteering), was done straight after breakfast, so we got it over and done with. Sadly, once again I was unfairly paired with Kevin. On the plus side we weren't in a maze, so there was no repeat of the Hampton court fiasco. At lunch, I had toad in the hole, which tasted adequate but nothing more. After lunch, we did abseiling, which was so much fun. It was funny watching Gene quake with fear coming off the lip at the top and losing nerve half way through and just hanging there with his eyes closed screaming. Richard, of course, cried, as the leaders told him to edge over the drop, then demanded to be exempt from the task. It was also enjoyable to see the leaders struggle to fit Kevin into a harness, eventually, giving up because they didn't have a kid sized xxxxl fatass available in their vast array of options. Adam Blackburn and I went down in tandem opposite each other doing commando jumps the whole way. We made it a race. Although Adam won, it was on a technicality. I was ahead of him the whole way, but the stupid harness fail safe kicked in when I took too large a commando jump and the wires and or harness emergency break stopped me, stalling me just before I reached the ground. After abseiling, we went to dinner where I ate cheeseburgers and fries, and found out the girls in our class have been secretly crafting together a Ouija board out of toilet paper (however, that worked I'll never know) and are trying to cast spells on guys they fancy. Also, this evening there was another joyous event I can tell you about. Dean Bronson, the school bully, got dumped by his long time (three week) girlfriend Sarah Washington. As I was walking back to my room I saw him crying near the tennis courts. Obviously, I had to tell everyone as this news is too good not to share. The king bully had been knocked off his throne. I was smart about it, though, concerned for my own safety, I changed the story to protect my identity. To this end, I covered my tracks by telling everyone, Richard told me he saw Dean Bronson crying near the tennis courts. Today has been a good day, so much so that I don't even mind filling in this infernal diary. But that's all you're getting from me today. Goodnight.

Day Five

This morning at breakfast, I saw Richard Slate at the next table. For some unknown reason, he seemed to have developed a fresh black eye overnight. I found this strange but Richard is strange, so I shan't question it. For breakfast, I ate a yoghurt and a banana. We are heading home today as it's Friday. This comes as a mild disappointment to me, but I know Gene is pleased as he foolishly spent all his money on tatty souvenirs at the gift shop on the first day and has been attempting to scav money off of everyone else since, presumably to buy more tatty souvenirs. Personally, I think he should have spent his money on spare underpants as he's been wearing the same single pair for a week. I for one won't miss the food in this place. After breakfast, we went on a short trip in the mini bus to the first settlement ever made in the Isle of Wight, which has now been turned into a museum tour. At one point, the tour guide said:

"We have a cow here named Beverly who gets milked every day," at which point, I leaned over to my friend Sian McPeake and whispered:

"Yeah, Beverly Walters the cow!" Sian burst into hysterics, it was brilliant. A little while later, the tour guide brought us to a well, where she talked about how this was where the village folk would go to gather their water and wash their clothes. I stuck my hand up and asked how deep the well was, but before she had time to answer, Steve spat a loogie down the well, and waited to hear it splash.

"About 30 ft I'd say," Steve said. The tour guide looked horrified. Aside from the cow and the well, I don't remember much about the tour, only to say that I think it's bad that tour guides are sometimes forced to wear matching era outfits. You don't go to NASA and have a tour guide by someone dressed as a rocket, yet this guide remained in her costume of a black pinafore throughout the tour. Sadly, she broke character when Steve spat in the well, so it broke the entire illusion and just made her look like a mental case in a cooks outfit. We finished the tour at around 12, and got back for some lunch. I had chicken and chips. The chicken was dry and the chips were cold. After lunch, we packed our bags and boarded the bus, which leads me to writing this in a hurry. I am currently sitting next to Steve who is anxiously waiting for me to finish so we can trade Pogs. I have nothing more to say anyway. So yeah, I'm done.

THE END

Chapter 15
Parents' Evening

In the Bible, we learn that in the last days, the sun will turn to darkness and the moon to blood. This is indeed terrifying imagery and a warning of things to come. As a kid, a similar occurrence happens once a year as Parents' evening encroaches ever closer.

Unlike today's millennial generation with their overprotective parents and molly coddling teachers who are too afraid to say anything negative about the child's learning for fear of parental reprisal, our generation didn't mess around. This 'no nonsense' approach only increased with my parents' generation and so on and so forth. Consequently, Parents' Evening became much more of a witch hunt than a time to relax on your laurels and enjoy an evening of praise. Of course, there would be the odd pathetic parent who would subscribe to the idea that their precious child could do no wrong. But as far as I was concerned, this was a life I never knew. For me, the opposite was more the case.

It was a bleak Thursday evening when we (my parents and I) entered the St Paul's School reception area, and I guardedly escorted them towards the main assembly hall where the teachers were all sitting at individual desks taking consultations. I scanned the room looking for familiar faces.

In the corner was Richard Slate sitting with his parents talking to Mrs Lawrence. Richard had already turned on the water works (crying not peeing) as a plea to get out of trouble for a possible negative remark from Mrs Lawrence. Richard really was pathetic, but more pathetic was that, although he seemed to play this hard done by crying game every day, the parents kept falling for it and consoling him. I later found out he was crying 'cuz he had not yet had a chance to pick up his weekly copy of

The Beano from the newsagent, despite the fact that the parents had promised him they'd swing by a newsagent on the way home and pick it up for him. He did the same thing for the same reason one day when he came around my house, except as well as tears he also threw a tantrum. The kid was a 10-year-old man and didn't have a shred of dignity. Naturally, I felt obliged to share this story with my classmates the next day, and he was justly bullied all through the week, which again ended in him crying. This kid never learned.

Continuing my survey of the room, I spotted Gene Colins next. He was sitting with his parents Sid and Amy. Sid, his dad, was a man who refused to get out of the 60s, and despite dressing up for the occasion still sported the same raggedy long greasy hair and long tufty beard, which remains with him to this day. I imagine he thought he scrubbed up pretty well, but to everyone else, he looked like a bum in a suit. Meanwhile, Gene sat constantly fidgeting on his chair like he had ants in his pants and kept checking his analogue watch like some kind of nervous tick, moving it back and forth to his ear to hear it tick, then tapping the watch face and tutting. To this day I reckon if he owned a fidget spinner back in the day, it may have sorted him out completely and his focus would be vastly improved. Sadly, they were not invented for another 20 years. But if…if he had had one, the difference I can imagine would be akin to the movie 'Sliding Doors'. Hell, Gene may have been a Wall Street trader or a successful lawyer with his own firm in another life.

Suddenly, I felt a prod in the back. I turned around sharply to see who it was. It was Ben Baker.

"Hey Sleggs, check these out. Got them today," he whispered, then lifted his right foot to show off his new pair of trainers. They were LA lights, and I got to hand it to him, they were very cool. They lit up with every step he took. Ben Baker was always showing off his latest gear, so I was used to it, but that didn't make me any less jealous.

"They're alright I guess," I said desperately trying to diffuse his ego.

"Alright? They're mint! Just 'cuz your parents wouldn't buy you them," he replied coldly.

"My dad's a doctor. I'm pretty sure he could afford to get me those if I wanted them," I came back.

"Yeah," he continued to whisper. "But your parents still wouldn't get you them 'cuz they don't love you," he answered back colder still.

"Oh piss off, Ben," I grunted, elbowing him in the solar plexus and he walked off wheezing.

In the middle of the room sat Kevin with his mum Pam. I hadn't noticed till my mum nudged me and said:

"Look, Michael, it's your best friend." I looked at her with annoyance, then quickly came back:

"Look mum, there's your husband," pointing to my dad who had wandered off and was flirting badly with one of the younger hot mums.

"John!" she snapped, and he scurried back to her side his tail between his legs.

I continued to stare at Kevin with a malignant look in my eye. He was sat next to his mum, Pam, talking to Miss Harris. Miss Harris kept attempting to have a conversation with Pam about Kevin's behaviour, hygiene, classroom etiquette and test scores which were all far below board, but every time she got half way through a sentence, Kevin would rudely interrupt like an excited puppy, unaware of his bad conduct, citing a random moment of achievement in his academic career, audaciously seeking praise. These achievements weren't even achievements. They were basic expected requirements of a student, like turning up back on time from lunch for class 3 days in a row or scoring 1 out of 10 in a spelling test. He shouted these accomplishments as if he wanted everyone in the room to be aware of his exemplarily efforts, like it would garner a standing ovation or something. To make matters worse after each silly statement uttered from his mouth, his mum would lavish him with praise and try to convince Miss Harris to play along. Eventually, the whole frustration of not being able to get a word in edge ways and the din of Kevin's loud raspy voice became too much for Miss Harris and she gave up, and ushered my family forwards.

As we took our seats, my dad stuck out his hand and introduced himself.

"Hi! I'm Doctor John Sleggs." He was always eager to introduce himself to others this way as a smug way of showing off his accomplishments as if the stethoscope he insisted on hanging around his neck wasn't already a dead enough give away. Miss Harris returned the greeting introducing herself and they shook hands.

She then began to rifle through some papers and prepare her opening statement. Next she tapped her fingers on the desk a few times over, which had me worried.

"Well, on the whole, it's been quite a successful year for Michael, and I'm very proud of his attitude," she said with a smile. I breathed a sigh of relief.

"But?" my dad pushed.

"There is no but. I mean, obviously he struggled a little this year to keep up and his test scores aren't quite what they used to be. They're still fairly good though. I think he deserves a little break as he's clearly had a hard time putting the pieces back since recovering from his stroke," she answered kindly.

"Nonsense, that was 3 months ago. He should be back on form; he will be back on form," my mum cut in bitterly.

"With all due respect, Mrs Sleggs, Michael has endured a lot of setbacks with his medical history. He is trying very hard, and we're all very proud of him, as I'm sure you are. I don't think adding further stress to his life by demanding the same results as before is really fair. These things take time. Like I said, he's still one of the top students, just not top top. But he has lots of friends and is very popular with everyone," Harris continued.

"School is not a popularity contest!" my mum sharply interjected.

"What do you have to say for yourself, Michael?" my dad said crossly leering at me with a look that had 'tonight's menu, spanking with a side of grounding' written on it.

"I dunno," I replied confused. It was as if they were deliberately choosing to ignore everything the teacher was saying and make up their own version, nit picking at the tiny fragments of slight failure from Harris' statement.

"You don't know!?" my dad repeated.

"Well, you heard the teacher, she's pleased with my learning, yes, I may not be up to scratch but, but, but…" I began to panic and turned into Gareth Gates on audition day. The truth was I wasn't really trying my hardest and I had no intention to. Earlier that year, I had suffered two major strokes during an open-heart surgery. One of the strokes twisted my leg, so I had to undergo 6 months of physiotherapy to walk normally again, albeit like a penguin, and the other effected my learning, making me forget everything I had learnt to that point and muddling up my process for working things out. I had been through similar setbacks in the past although this was the worst, and by now, I just didn't care anymore. I was literally of the mindset that 'I'll do what I need to get by' no more, no less. To this day, I hold the same principal unless I'm actually interested in something and want to learn more about it. As far as academia and schooling is concerned, I still believe that once you get past a certain point, it usually becomes a pointless, inane and futile exercise and is by no way a yardstick to measure someone's capability for a job. Fortunately, after generations of being stuck in the old system of things, I think the world is finally beginning to see it my way too. Someone's grades and certificates are no sign that they are better equipped at achieving a certain career than someone without those things. I can't blame my parents for seeing it otherwise though, as for them, academic success and career achievement went hand in hand as it had done for generations before. I can, however, blame them for not cutting me any slack. I was 10 years old for goodness sake, and I had been through my own personal Vietnams more times than Rambo.

Moments later, my parents grabbed my arm and snatched me away from the table, thanking Miss Harris for her input and we made our way to the exit.

"Did you hear what she said, Michael?" my mum spitted.

"I have never been so embarrassed in all my life," my dad added.

"Your dad's a doctor, and you…" she paused, "well, I can't even stand to look at you right now; I'm so ashamed." She continued. I had had enough, I tugged my arms from their clutches, turned around to face them. We were back in the reception by this point, and no one else was around.

"What the hell is wrong with you guys?" I yelled, "Did you not hear what Miss Harris said? That I'm a good pupil, still scoring above average. Just because I'm not a genius so what? Surely what matters is that I'm a decent person. You two are so stuck up, it's disgusting. It's all about 'oh what will everyone think?' So here's a tip, if you're so ashamed about my schoolwork, don't tell them! I'm so tired of this bullshit!" I finished. It was the first time I ever swore at my parents. That night we drove home in silence. I went straight to my room and slammed the door. I expected one or both of them to enter at some point to bollock me, but they never came. I guess for once they decided to listen to me and instead of enforcing the law took pity on my pain. It didn't last though. It never did. Throughout my school years, I was constantly berated for my scores, though, in fairness, they did keep dropping but levelled out at average. What's interesting is if you look back now, there is a direct correlation to bollocking and unabashed shaming to score drop. Maybe I required a bit of encouragement. Maybe I was being a brat. I guess we'll never know.

Chapter 16
Sports Day

I was never a massive fan of Sports Day as I was never really very athletic as a kid. Also, the only sports I really excelled at, Basketball and Baseball, weren't on the curriculum due to their American heritage. I'm not sure how it ended up this way, but I've always had a massive disdain for football and cricket and find them extremely boring. The idea of chasing around a ball for 90 minutes in shorts, and overreacting in pain massively every time I trip over or get tackled, which is the basic structure of any typical FIFA game never really appealed to me, nor did the pompous and slightly effeminate la-di-da of cricket. I appreciate I exist in a tiny minority of British outsiders and voicing my opinions here is sure to get me in trouble by some snowflakes who don't think rationally about someone expressing an opposing opinion. It's not my intention to offend, so if I do, please, place the blame on yourself for being such a pussy before you point it my way. Thank you.

To be honest, I don't know why I brought all that up anyway, as, whilst football and cricket are British sports, they weren't present or accounted for during sports day. Sports Day was mainly reserved for running. Sure, there was all also the sideline events of egg and spoon races, sack races and wheelbarrow races (this was team effort where one child would lift another child's legs up whilst they both ran forwards, one on their feet, the other on their hands), but they didn't really count. Alas, they were the only ones I stood a chance in. Due to my crippled heart, I was at a massive disadvantage in my early years from a cardio perspective and could never keep up with my classmates when it came to the 100m sprint. What made matters worse, however, was that the teachers knew this and so in an effort to level the playing field, gave me a 25m head start, which would have been humiliating as is but for the added bonus of still coming last place in spite of this. For what it's worth I did get off lightly. I figure if it had been anyone else, they would have been mocked relentlessly for this astounding athletic ineptitude. To pour petrol on the fire, Sports Day was parents inclusive. They would stand at the sidelines cheering everyone on and awing me as I limped my way over the finish line 10 seconds later than everyone else.

Sooner or later, my race for last place would inevitably be over, and I'd watch on the sidelines whilst the other classes went through the motions till we'd proceed in the other side events I spoke about earlier.

First, the egg and spoon race. This was easy as long as you kept your cool. It relied more on balance than speed which meant it may give me an upper hand if I had the right opponents. Mrs Rudley shuffled through her pre-assigned tables.

"Next up. Egg and Spoon race. Taking part, Adam Blackburn, Ben Baker, Kevin Blankenhorn, Michael Sleggs and Gene Colins. Take your positions please," Mrs Rudley boomed over her speaker microphone. *Thank goodness,* I thought to myself, as I took my place behind the line. Gene was particularly clumsy, and Kevin, well I didn't know how Kevin would fair, but it couldn't have been that good. Worst case scenario I wouldn't come dead last.

"On your marks. Get set. GO!" screamed Mrs Rudley.

We all set off and Gene, all too eager with his speed, almost immediately dropped his egg, eliminating him from the race.

"Bad luck, son," his dad consoled off to my right as Gene skulked off the track. A brief under the breath scoff left my mouth which left me unbalanced, but I quickly regained my composure. About ten seconds into the race, Adam was near the finish line, I'm glad he was beating Ben as his arrogance rarely went unpunished. I was already stoked I was not going to be consigned last place thanks to Gene's unwieldy, blundering, bumbling, bungling, butterfingered, ham handed, graceless skill, and I now noticed Kevin and I were neck and neck. This was my moment, to secure 3rd place, a position I had only dreamed about for years was now looking like a very possible outcome if cards were played right. I increased my speed slightly to take the lead. Kevin chased in hot pursuit, wobbling the spoon worryingly to recalibrate his balance. The concentration on our faces akin to those NASA geniuses awaiting radio reconnection with the Apollo 13 crew on the last part of the return journey. I kept focused, with a straight face. Kevin, on the other hand, had his tongue hanging low out of his open mouth, occasionally wiggling from side to side, as if it were the balance re-correction gimbal for his hand. He caught up quick, and we were now moments away from the finish line. 5 meters... 4. Sweat pulsed down Kevin's greasy hairline to his forehead, and his tongue switched between gimbaling and panting; meanwhile, I kept my reserve. 3 meters... 2, we were so close. Suddenly, I heard a loud cry coming from my left.

"OH NO!" Kevin, tripping over his undone shoelace lost his balance, but not just of the egg and spoon but of his entire body and collapsed to the floor like a fat sweaty oaf.

"Timber," I heard someone call from the outskirts as I crossed the finish line triumphantly in 3rd place. Kevin lay still on the ground for a couple of seconds, as the egg rolled away, out of control, till it eventually stopped at Pam's (Kevin's mum's) foot. She picked it up and snuck it into her handbag. Eventually, Kevin heaved his plump body from ground. The grass had been freshly mowed the day before, so Kevin was covered in it which added further joy to my victory as I watched him struggle to remove random tufts of tumbleweed from his hair occasionally mistaking his own knotted clumps for strands of grass and giving himself a little shock at the pain of the tug.

A few other events followed which I wasn't involved in, until the wheelbarrow race. Nervously I peered over Mrs Rudley's shoulder in an attempt to read who she was pairing me with for the race in order to mentally prepare myself. She spied me in her peripherals and quickly jolted the piece of paper to her chest obstructing my view. I don't know why, it wasn't the nuclear football for crying out loud and I'd soon find out anyway. It was clear that drawing any kindness from her was like drawing blood from a stone. At last, the time came.

"Right everybody, if I could have your attention, the next event is the boys' wheelbarrow race." Mrs Rudley snapped. "Pairs are as follows. Adam Blackburn with Ben Baker. John Chomsky with Adam Daniels. Michael Sleggs with Kevin Blankenhorn. Gene Colins with Steve McDougal. You have one minute to decide your positions."

With that Kevin fell to the floor like he'd been shot in the head. He then immediately started mule kicking, indicating for me to pick his legs up. Meanwhile, my opponents graciously conferred amongst themselves as to whom was best suited for which role. Being paired with Kevin clearly didn't afford me that debate due to his pig-headed nature. Reluctantly, I grabbed Kevin's hoofs off the ground and prepared myself. Coincidentally, at this point, all the blood rushed to Kevin's face, which, now more than ever adopted the physical appearance of a pig head too. Mrs Rudley started counting down.

"Ready, steady, squashed bananas," she joked over the speaker which was met with silence save for a solitary isolated cough from a member of the audience. Kevin paced a few yards forwards on his hands dragging me along with his legs.

"Ah, ah, I got you, Kevin." Mrs Rudley smiled pointing him out to the crowd still desperately trying to land a laugh.

"Good stuff. Okay. On your marks. Get set. Go!"

We set off, Ben and Adam once again taking the lead followed closely behind by Adam Daniels and John Chomsky. Chomsky, who was on the ground, was scuttling along like a spider with his spindly arms; meanwhile, a couple yards ahead of them, Ben who was on the ground in his pair was using his arms to gallop along like a Gazelle. On my right-hand side stood Steve who was driving Gene so fast every few meters Gene would buckle and fall head over ass, so Steve had to keep backing up to regain the correct position.

"Bloody hell, Gene!" I heard Steve mumble under his breath in sheer frustration after the third fall. At the same time, I was struggling with my own cumbersome, lumbering wheelbarrow who plodded along slowly but thankfully without error. It was now like the race of the tortoise and the hare. Each time Gene tumbled, it bought Kevin and I enough seconds to temporarily catch up. Once again, I found us neck and neck with our opponents with 5 meters to go. 4 meters… 3. Gene buckled again. Kevin and I waddled past to 2 meters… 1. Suddenly, I came to a halt, Kevin paused to scratch his nose. Then turned his head back to me to inform me of what I just witnessed.

"Had an itchy nose, had to scratch it," he sniffed. The delay had cost us valuable seconds. Gene and Steve had regained their shape and position and steamed past us.

"MOVE!" I screamed at Kevin holding his legs further apart and kicking him in the bollocks, like I was a furious farmer and they were the engine of some knackered tractor in winter. Kevin squealed like a pig, adding further credence to the pig head metaphor I used a while back, and began plodding forwards, but a second too late. Steve and Gene crossed the finish line in third place, consigning Kevin and I to last. I was livid, and threw Kevin's legs to floor, kicking his foot in a rage, he retaliated in an infantile petty manner by trying to kick me in the shins as I walked away, missing me by a mile.

At the end of the day, things were rounded up by the novelty dad race. I don't remember much of it, I couldn't tell you who won and I doubt my dad was even there to be honest. All I can recall is a disturbing memory of Daniel Parker's dad absolutely bumming himself (not actually bumming himself, this is a metaphor for arrogant, unabashed, narcissistic behaviour), flexing his muscles like he was Mr Universe to an audience of confused mums, all the while wearing ridiculous hot pink running shorts. I also recollect seeing him at one point consuming a packet of Smiths Salt 'n' Shake crisps (side note, Smiths has since been bought out by Walkers) and watching him as he disposed of the fully intact unused blue salt sachet in the bin, probably as part of some stupid healthy eating campaign he was on. This only served to aggravate me further. All in all, the day had been a disaster, but what did I expect, it was Sports Day, and I was Michael Sleggs.

Chapter 17
Disco Night

Our final year at St Paul's Primary School was coming to an end. The week before splitting up for summer (to be followed by our slow, laborious and cruel continued path through the school system in secondary school), we were gifted with a school disco. It was a social event exclusively for the final year to celebrate the end of year and the end of an era. There had been much chat about chosen outfits, plans to make a move on crushes, and secret scheming to spike the punch bowl with alcohol (by the more rebellious kids) in the hallways in the weeks leading up to the event. For me, none of this stuff mattered too much, as long as there was a good spread of fizzy pop and sweets. We were still in that innocent age where we were never too self-conscious, and being insecure never really occurred to us unless something unbelievably embarrassing happened (like the time I had to do P.E in my sister's frilly pink panties). Sadly, little did we know everything would change in secondary school, and the adolescent years of unbearable awkwardness and humiliation at the slightest difference between oneself and one's pack of sheep friends would kick in.

It was 7 pm, and I entered the school hall like a pimp dressed in my black Herbie jeans and red spliffy T-shirt acting like I was an OG. Whigfield Saturday Night was blasting throughout the hall and, standing on either side of the room, the boys and girls were spilt like the red sea. Straight ahead stood Mrs Harris and Mrs Rudley, one manning the stereo and being the proverbial DJ, the other manning the buffet spread of sweeties, crisps and soft drinks. Nervously I made my way down the centre of the room towards the buffet throwing down a couple of dance moves along the way in an awkward balance of confidence and embarrassment. I made it clear I wasn't taking myself too seriously though just in case people were actually judging me by the skill of my dancing, which left much to be desired. After what seemed like an hour (but was probably mere seconds) in the proverbial viper pit of centre stage, I reached the food table, grabbed a paper plate and started piling on snacks. Next, I approached the drinks section where Mrs Rudley was rationing out tiny paper cups of Coke, Fanta and Sprite. I grabbed a cup of coke and was about to make my way back to my mates on the left side of the hall when Mrs Rudley spoke.

"I'm not gonna get any mischief out of you this evening, am I, Michael?" she grunted. I turned back to face her.

"No, why would you assume that?" I replied, confused.

"You know why!" she responded with a silly smile on her face. I looked at her more bewildered than ever.

"Mrs Rudley, are you drunk?" I asked.

"No!" she shot back. "It was a joke, relax," she then added laughing to herself.

"Oh, well, it wasn't funny," I said, her faced dropped. "Don't quit your day job, Rudders," I continued, then, munched a crisp in front of her in an affronting, arrogant manner, before spinning around on one heel, like a boss, nodding my head to the beat of the song and sauntering on towards my mates. I'm not going to lie, it was pretty slick, and I knew it. I approached Sam, Adam, Andrew and Stephen.

"Alright boys?" I said, greeting my mates and nodding simultaneously.

"Alright, Sleggsy?" they replied, almost in chorus. I made myself comfortable, leaning my back against the wall standing next to Adam, who was wearing a grey Fred Perry jumper and jeans.

"How's it going?" Adam asked.

"Um, yeah good," I responded quickly trying to fill the void of silence, "You?"

"Yeah good," he replied.

"Cool," I answered, adding another 'cool' quickly at a lower volume, then swiftly taking a sip out of my cup of coke.

"What you been up to since school, Michael?" Steve questioned poking his head around Adam.

"You mean for the past four hours?" I returned.

"Yeah," Steve eagerly came back.

I sucked in a deep breath hoping to come up with some big answer but couldn't think of anything special and puffed the air back out.

"Um, just sorta got ready for this I guess," I came back with a slightly puzzled look on my face.

"Oh," Steve leaned back against the wall. "Makes sense," he finished, seemingly disappointed. We all leaned back against the wall silently, trying to look busy, whilst occasionally peering at the late stragglers who were still arriving and the group of girls congregating at the other side of the hall, whispering to themselves then throwing out the occasional chuckle. It was all a little unnerving and paranoia inducing but all part of growing up I suppose. A moment later the room was filled with an over powering waft of Lynx Atlantis as school bully Dean Bronson sashayed in like he owned the place wearing a cheap blue polyester suit, white shirt and clip on tie. His hair was greased back like he had just walked out of a casting call for the movie Wall Street. On his way towards our group he spotted Gene, who was wearing Champion sweat pants and a white ALF T-shirt, and jumping around the room holding streamers. A moment later, he jumped into Dean's path and got shoved violently against the wall for the infraction. Dean then snatched the streamers out of his hands then snapped them in half over his knee whilst Gene stood by, his chin beginning to wobble.

"Dean, don't be a arse!" Sam interrupted.

"What you say, Sam?" Dean responded hostilely dropping the remainder of the streamers to the floor and getting up in Sam's grill.

"Back off, Dean, I'm here to enjoy the party, like everyone else, that's all," Dean peered down the line at the rest of us who were observing the altercation, and I guess he must have felt outnumbered or didn't want to cause a fuss because he actually gave the decision some thought for once and decided to walk away. He went and grabbed some food then joined the rest of the lads against the wall, next to me.

I sniffed the air and started choking.

"What is it, Sleggs?" Dean snapped like I was ruining the atmosphere.

"Nothing, just your deodorant is a bit overpowering, mate," I wheezed, only adding 'mate' to alleviate any hostile vibe of the statement. I certainly didn't consider Dean a mate.

"Get lost Sleggs, it's Lynx and the ladies love it," Dean spitted venomously.

"Oh," I said rolling my eyes, but carefully out of his line of sight, so he couldn't tell I was making fun.

"How much are you wearing?" I quizzed.

"10!" Dean responded.

"Sprays?" I followed up.

"Cans!" he replied, taking a deep swig of his cup of pop before crushing it in his hand and taking a badly formed basketball toss with it at the bin, which missed. He saw it miss, but instead of taking care of it, slowly sighed and rested his head on the wall behind him. No sooner had he done this, then Mrs Rudley screeched.

"Dean, pick that up and put it in the bin immediately."

Desperate to maintain his bad boy image to the very end, Dean responded:

"Make me!"

The music stuttered to a halt, and there was a collective, "Oooooooo," among the kids from both sides of the hall. Mrs Rudley marched over to Dean and barked.

"I beg your pardon!?"

"You heard me, make me!" Dean reasserted confidently. We all watched with bated breath.

"Dean, you have two choices," Mrs Rudley began, taking off her jacket and throwing it on an empty patch of the food table, then rolling up her sleeves like the beginning of an intimidating CIA interrogation. "You can either throw that cup in the bin properly, or you can throw yourself out of the disco," Rudley continued her nostrils flaring.

"Fine," Dean replied after an intense stare out with Rudley, and walked towards the cup, but then suddenly turned sharply and flipped the table of snacks petulantly. "Didn't wanna be at this gay disco anyway," he continued.

"Get out!" Mrs Rudley squealed furiously! Dean turned towards the door and left as quickly as he arrived.

"Well, that was exciting," I chuckled. "Shame they're still gonna have to fumigate the building to get rid of the lynx cloud."

As Dean left, we heard him thump a door in aggression in the background, followed by an "Ow!" then no more.

The music started up again and besides the mess of snacks on the floor near the flipped tables the party was back in swing.

At 7:45 pm, Kevin showed up unfashionably late. He was wearing brown corduroys and a green turtle neck, the whole outfit looked far too tight and his man boobs and belly were clearly defining the bulk of it. He took one look at the overturned table of food and sulked over to the drinks to grab what he could out of the few rations that were left.

"Nice outfit, Kev," I scoffed.

"What's wrong with it?" Kevin grunted back.

"Oh, nothing, just…brave," I added another chuckle.

"It's called fashion, Michael, you could learn something," he came back.

"Says who? Tony Hart?" I returned geniously. Kevin tried to kick me, but I grabbed his leg in the process and dragged him across the floor as he kept pace by hopping as fast as he could on his other foot. I dragged him as far as the door then let him go. He was livid and tried to kick me a second time, but this time I was too quick and dodged it; meanwhile, there was the sound of big tear as Kevin lost balance and ended up doing the splits on the floor, clearly the tension of his fat thighs behind the material had been too much to sustain and a gaping whole appeared in the groin of the pants. Kevin yelped, his body was never built to do this kind of manoeuvre, and from the splits, he toppled over sideways till he got into a position where he could scissor his legs shut and regain his feet. By this point, I was back over by the wall, talking to Adam.

"Adam, you can breakdance, right?" I asked already knowing the answer was yes.

"Um, yeah a little I guess," he responded coyly.

"You should do some." I said, indicating to the dance floor with my head.

"Uh, not right now, Mike," he replied, it was clear he was shy about his talent.

"Go on, admittedly no one's gonna expect you to be as adept as Kev doing the splits over there, but it's a cool skill, the chicks'll find it impressive," I encouraged, patting him on the back.

"Yeah alright," Adam conceded and made his way to the centre of the dance floor. What followed was the most awkward and slow display of basic break dancing I've ever seen in my life. Adam went to on all fours and slowly followed a circle, using his hands as a compass point, and his legs to crawl around, occasionally and very carefully swapping the position of his hands to accommodate for the amount of degrees he'd travelled around his circle. I'm not going to lie, Adam's a great friend, but this was embarrassing. He'd let me down, he'd let other boys down and most of all, he'd let himself down. After one complete circle, I quickly rescued him from the floor.

"Wait, there's more, don't you want to see…" Adam eagerly explained as I rushed him back to the wall.

"No Adam, I've seen enough," I said in a cruel Simon Cowell-esque tone.

"Oh well, did it look good?" Adam stuttered, desperate for some praise. I sighed, I couldn't tell him the truth, it'd break his heart to know he looked like an autistic starfish having some kind of convulsion.

"It looked great, Adam, very impressive!" I patted him on the back and looked at Sam shaking my head in contradiction to my words.

"I knew it!" Adam said proudly raising his eyebrows in a deluded sense of confidence.

The hours clocked by, and by the end of the evening, everyone's courage had grown, and we were all out on the dance floor boogying. One had to admit, as square as the teachers were, they had picked out a great playlist that night. Scatman, Hanson, Take That, Haddaway, The Outhere Brothers and even some PJ and Duncan had taken us on a rip-roaring disco journey and everyone had had a great time, including Gene who had recovered from his body slam and found some new streamers to frolic around with. Even Kevin had stopped hobbling around in recovery from his forced splits, and whilst he still looked at state, having also spilt coke down his top at some point and was continuously belching; he seemed to be having a good time. There had been a couple of awkward slow dances in which we boys had paired up with girls and danced slowly at the maximum distance to each other whilst still holding onto the shoulders or waist of the partner and desperately avoiding eye contact. Right before the very last song, we were all given party poppers to inaugurate the occasion. The final song played. It was 'Stay another day' by East 17, fitting for the occasion as it added a touch of pathos and nostalgia to the era that was coming to a close. As the song finished in the epic church bell way that it does, we all cheered and set off our party poppers. The two teachers applauded and wished everyone well as we slowly departed from the gym. It was 8:30 pm, closing time. At this point, Richard Slate entered the nearly empty hall with its streamers, poppers and odd food waste littering its floor. He nudged me on my way out.

"Where's everyone going? The party's just started, right?" he asked in a panic.

"No, Richard, party's over, it started at 7 pm, and we've just finished," he teared up almost instantaneously.

"What do you mean?" he whimpered. I shook my head then added:

"To be honest, mate, I think you should be counting your blessings. You wouldn't have lasted long in that get up." He was wearing grey trousers and an Austin Powers style Jabot blouse.

"Oh, shut up, Sleggs," he said in a grump and punched me in the arm. I brushed it off and walked out to the reception where all the parents were waiting to pick up their kids, leaving Richard behind me, his head slumped in sadness facing the hall, as the reception door closed behind him, like the ending of the Godfather.

Chapter 18
The Last Day of School

On the last day of any term or school year, we were allowed to bring in toys from home to play with. On this day, the school would do no teaching of any kind and operate as more of a crèche than anything else. Of course, there was still the formalities of a morning and special afternoon assembly to attend. The afternoon assembly doubled up as a small graduation ceremony where we were all gifted with Youth Bibles with the school's motto emblazed on the inside. I say emblazed. It was more just a small postcard-sized piece of paper with a drawing of kids doing 'ring around a rosie' and the motto 'Steadfast in the Faith' pritt-sticked inside the front page. That day I brought in my Gameboy as it was the best toy I had and bragging rights were all the rage. Naturally, I was still upstaged by 'spoilt brat' Ben Baker, who brought in his Nintendo Gameboy, Sega Game gear and even his Sega Master system which he hooked up to the classroom TV. In fairness to him, he was quite good at sharing but that still didn't negate the fact that he was living like a Rockefeller with his toys, whilst the rest of us peasants would have to beg and plead for a mere morsel from our tight-fisted parents.

The morning assembly was quite standard, a few songs and prayers, a little anecdote that related to a life lesson, the usual stuff. However, this particular morning was special. As part of a prank, all the children in our year had decided to use the last song as a delivery message of our true feelings towards our enforced incarceration at St Paul's. To this end, when the time came, the song 'All things bright and beautiful, all creatures great and small' was adapted to:

One more day of school.
One more day of sorrow.
One more day of this old dump.
We'll be at home tomorrow.

This was met with a very disgruntled look on all the teachers' faces who were secretly holding back the laughter and a joint group tittering amongst us kids. We knew we had the upper hand. It was the last day. What were they going to do about it? They couldn't tell us all off. We piled out of the hall, and back to class. I pulled my Gameboy out of my backpack and started playing Donkey Kong Land. Within minutes, I had a group of backseat drivers/players crowding my screen and telling me what to do. They blocked out any light to the screen with their cumbersome shadows making it impossible to play. As much as I appreciated the attention, it wasn't adding anything to the gameplay and I began swatting them away like flies. Gene didn't seem to get the hint, even after the fifth time. I ended up slapping him away. He relentlessly kept creeping over my shoulder as often as he could to get a second viewing. I soon snapped, and in an act of petty vengeance, I turned the Gameboy off and shoved it back in my bag. In hindsight like most of my pathetic attempts to seek a reprisal in primary school, I was cutting off my nose to spite my face.

For Richard, the last day of school was like winning a ticket to Willy Wonka's Chocolate Factory. His parents lived in the Stone Age and as such didn't own a TV, much less allow him to have any games consoles. Going around his house was a big mistake. The hours always dragged as the only things to do were play a board game, Subbuteo, listen to the Archers on the radio, or if you were very lucky, play Scalectrix. Anyway, because of Richard's TV and video-game starved brain, the unbridled freedom of being able to see and interact with proper toys for once became an almost dangerous concoction. In these days, he would become snatchy and obnoxious which would inevitably end in him being physically restrained like a possessed mad man, which ultimately would finish the way things always did with Richard, in floods of tears, followed by an onslaught of justified teasing.

At snack time, we were all forced like prisoners to go outside to get some exercise. I made my way to the playground and spotted Kelly Stark and Lee Filton (the second most hard and scary kid in the school after Dean) chasing Gene Colins around the play park area. It looked like they were having fun, but as I got closer, I realised they were actually on a mission of intimidation. There was no rhyme or reason for it. It was merely bully vs weak kid. I should have just walked away, or better yet, defended Gene. But my crush on Kelly at the time got the better of me, and I joined the pack of wolves for the hunt. In my defence, I didn't mean any harm, and part of me thought it was childish fun, although clearly Gene was terrified. We ended up flanking him at the climbing frame and as I approached Gene said seven words that broke my heart.

"Michael, I thought you were my friend?" he whimpered clearly distressed and saddened by my actions. I knew right then and there I was making a mistake and could feel the guilt and shame wrap itself tight around me. Unfortunately, I was still in the presence of Lee and Kelly and not wanting to come off weak myself. I made the unconscionable decision of replying, "In your dreams," and even chuckled deviously after. I literally felt I had just made a deal with the Devil as I saw the devastation on Gene's face. I couldn't face him anymore and walked away whilst Lee and Kelly pummelled him.

A few minutes later, I had forgotten all about it and felt right as rain. I joined Alex Carter and kicked a football around with him till the end of break. This peace of mind was not to last though.

I hadn't been back in the classroom more than five minutes when Mrs Rudley approached me and Kelly and said Mrs Butterworth wanted to see us in her office. Her office had recently moved from an older building near the front of the school, to the school library for a temporary period whilst repairs were done on the old building. I knew she was in the library but in a futile, nervous attempt to buy myself time, I questioned the location several times, till my intentions of trying to run out of the clock became abundantly clear. Kelly and I entered the school Library (aka Mrs Butterworth's office) tentatively. Side note: rumour has it the Library was haunted by Rebecca Powell, a former student of St Paul's School who apparently died in the

1800s. Why a child ghost would choose to haunt a primary school I'll never know… a Toys R Us maybe, but not a school. As it happened, there was a situation about to unfold in the room far scarier than any ghost. As Kelly and I turned the corner around a shelf of books, we spotted Lee sitting on one side of a table and Gene and Mrs Butterworth on the other. Immediately, the penny dropped, as did our bowels.

"Kelly, Michael, take a seat," Mrs Butterworth said calmly. We looked at each other worryingly and did as we were told.

"I wish this conversation didn't have to happen on your last day, but I've heard some very disappointing news," she continued. I cleared my throat anxiously.

"It's come to my attention that you kids were bullying Gene at break time. What have you got to say for yourselves?" she said with a more cross tone than before. Stupidly, I tried to play it dumb and add a little levity to the situation by smiling and saying:

"We were playing tag, Gene must have just misinterpreted it."

"Does this look like chase to you!" she said, pointing out the Chinese burn on Genes arm. I swallowed my pride.

"Sorry Gene, I thought we were just messing around," my pupils where dilated and eyes opened wide, more from fear of Mrs Butterworth then the sight of a Chinese burn. I had seen a million of those in my life.

"I am hugely disappointed in the lot of you, especially you, Michael, I have never seen this behaviour from you," Mrs Butterworth went on furiously.

"I know, I know, I'm so sorry, it won't happen again," I folded like a paper house. Meanwhile, Lee sat there sniggering to himself. I couldn't believe the balls on this kid, he had only been at the school a year and was already challenging Dean's notoriety for being the biggest bully in the school. Kelly jumped in with her two cents.

"To be fair, Miss, Lee was the ringleader. He was the one doing the beatings. It was mostly all his fault," she rolled over on him, which puzzled me. Maybe she was just as scared as I and was clawing for a lesser sentence or maybe she just wanted to get back to her toys. I saw Kelly in town the other day and questioned her about this and she had no recollection of the event. I found it strange that a memory so vivid to me had completely escaped her brain. My only theory is that such a stressful event as being in Mrs Butterworth's office for a bollocking probably caused months of Vietnam flashbacks, which, in turn, led to her parents sending her to counselling and hypnotherapy to forget it. I should be so lucky.

"Is this true, Gene, was it mostly Lee?" Mrs Butterworth asked him. I looked at Gene, my eyes pleading with him to say yes and get us off the hook, although I didn't deserve it.

"Yeah I guess so," he replied softly, probably thinking that the recourse of one bully was better than three. I wouldn't have touched him after that anyway, and neither would Kelly I don't think, but I guess he didn't know that.

"Okay, Michael, Kelly, you're dismissed, but I don't ever want to hear about this happening again," Mrs Butterworth barked, and we got up promptly and walked away.

"Well, what do you have to say for yourself," I heard Mrs Butterworth snap in the background and looked behind one last time to see Lee putting his hands on his ears and mockingly repeat the words the Head had just asked him. If ever the phrase 'little shit' applied, this was it. I took a big sigh and left the room with massive pit stains from nervous sweat. Heading back to class I joined Adam Blackburn who was playing an Aladdin tiger electronic game he had brought in. In the corner, I saw John Chomsky trying to explain the rules of chess to Kevin,. It was an exhausting process, and he had been at it since the start of the day. Kevin just sat there looking dumb and chewing on an egg of glow-in-the-dark silly putty Andrew Murphy had brought in, which Kevin had mistaken for bubble gum. Meanwhile, Adam noticed the shot nerves on my face, but wasn't sure what had just happened or where I'd been. In a kindly bid to calm me down, he stopped playing with his game for a moment and handed me a straw and a piece of paper. Adam and I had sat together all year in Mrs Rudley's class and had become good friends. We often made each other laugh by launching wet paper wads (spitballs) through straws onto the ceiling. By the end of the year, the ceiling was covered and no one had noticed. Obviously, we were careful with our timing and only did it when the teacher wasn't looking. Pretty soon, the lunch bell rang for the last time, and we all packed outside to play one last time. I was always a bit sadder and pensive about things than my peers and chose to use the time to walk myself around the schoolyard in a dignified, grown up moment of acknowledgement of the occasion. Obviously, this didn't do much but isolate me as I wandered in solitude with my head held high in a disgusting gesture of pretentiousness whilst my friends all played out on the field like normal kids. After lunch, we went straight to assembly for the final time, for an hour-long special goodbye, which included the generic slideshows of our time at St Paul's, a few more songs and prayers, boring speeches with 'life after primary school' advice and a Bible and handshake from Mrs Butterworth and then it was finished. It seemed strange to me to be receiving a Bible and a handshake from the very women who only a couple of hours ago had me in her office for a massive bollocking. I tried to avoid eye contact when the transaction took place in order to alleviate some of the tension. I since realise that the fact that she had told me off was probably no big deal to her, and she genuinely wished me the best. But my child-like brain assumed she'd be holding onto the fury for years to come. If there's one thing I miss from childhood, it's the fact that everything seems so big and out of proportion to its reality. Whilst this isn't great when it comes to fears, it's amazing when it comes to hopes and dreams, and the world in which we live. Everything is possible when you're a kid. Everything is an opportunity. There is no such thing as impossible, and the world doesn't start and finish in a small bubble. It's as vast as you want it to be, and along with that come the emotions, like the overwhelming excitement for Christmas or birthdays on the horizon, or the wonder of nature. The greatest tragedy of growing up is getting stuck in a rut and seeing the world and the thrill of life through a pinhole, whereas before it was seen in IMAX. I don't know why it has to be this way, but I hope this book will hopefully reawaken some of those memories for you. I'm under no illusion that reading this will be life changing. That's ridiculous. But maybe it'll recapture something, perhaps a funny story that's laid dormant in the recesses of your mind since school, and you'll be inspired to write a story about that. Either way, dear reader, I hope you've enjoyed this dysfunctional trip through my early years and can relate to at least some of the stories written in these pages.

CPSIA information can be obtained
at www.ICGtesting.com
Printed in the USA
BVHW041444070720
583184BV00006B/84